Ella Rea Carroll

From my Grandmother
Christmas 1918.

OVER PARADISE RIDGE

[See page 122

"I GOT A CALL—A LAND CALL THAT I HAD TO
ANSWER"

OVER PARADISE RIDGE

RIDGE

A ROMANCE

BY

MARIA THOMPSON DAVIESS

AUTHOR OF
THE MELTING OF MOLLY, Etc.

ILLUSTRATED

NEW YORK
GROSSET & DUNLAP
PUBLISHERS

Published by Arrangement with Harper & Brothers

TO
BERNICE LANIER DICKINSON

CONTENTS

ILLUSTRATIONS

OVER PARADISE RIDGE

I

NOBODY knows what starts the sap along the twigs of a very young, tender, and green woman's nature. In my case it was Samuel Foster Crittenden, though how could he have counted on the amount of Grandmother Nelson that was planted deep in my disposition, ready to spring up and bear fruit as soon as I was brought in direct acquaintance with a seed-basket and a garden hoe? Also why should Sam's return to a primitive state have forced my ancestry up to the point of flowering on the surface? I do hope Sam will not have to suffer consequences, but I can't help it if he does. What's born in us is not our fault.

"Yes, Betty, I know I'm an awful shock to you as a farmer. I ought to have impressed it on you more thoroughly before you—you saw me in the act. I'm sorry, dear," Sam comforted me gently and tenderly as I wept with dismay into the sleeve of his faded blue overalls.

"I can't understand it," I sniffed as I held on to his sustaining hand while I balanced with him on the top of an old, moss-covered stone wall he had begged me to climb to for a view of Harpeth Valley which he thought might turn my attention from him. "Have you mislaid your beautiful ambitions anywhere?"

"I must have planted them along with my corn crop, I reckon," he answered, quietly, as he steadied his shoulder against an old oak-tree that grew close to the fence and then steadied my shoulder against his.

"It is just for a little while, to get evidence about mud and animals and things like that, isn't it?" I asked, with great and undue eagerness, while an early blue jay flitted across from tree-top to tree-top in so happy a spirit that I sympathized with the admiring lady twit that came from a bush near the wall. "You are going back out into the world where I left you, aren't you?"

"No," answered Sam, in an even tone of voice that quieted me completely; it was the same he had used when he made me stand still the time his fish-hook caught in my arm at about our respective sixth and tenth years. "No, I'm going to be just a farmer. It's this way, Betty. That valley you are looking down into has the strength to feed hundreds of thousands of hungry men, women, and children when they come down to us over Paradise Ridge from the crowded old world; but men have to make her give it up and be ready for them. At first I wasn't sure I could, but now I'm going to put enough heart and brain and muscle into my couple of hundred acres to dig out my share of food, and that of the other folks a great strapping thing like I am ought to help to feed. I'll plow your name deep into the potato-field, dear," he ended, with a laugh, as he let go my hand, which he had almost dislocated while his eyes smoldered out over the Harpeth Valley, lying below us like an earthen cup full of green richness, on whose surface floated a cream of mist.

"It just breaks my heart to see you away from everything and everybody, all burned up and scratched up and muddy, and—and—" I was saying as he lifted me back into the road again beside my shiny new Redwheels that looked like an enlarged and very gay sedan-chair.

"Look, look, Betty!" Sam interrupted my distress over his farmer aspect, which was about to become tearful, and his eyes stopped regarding me with sad seriousness and lit with affectionate excitement as he peered into the bushes on the side of the road. "There's my lost heifer calf! You run your car on up to my house beyond the bend there and I'll drive her back through the woods to meet you. Get out and head her off if she tries to pass you." With which command he was gone just as I was about to begin to do determined battle for his rescue.

I did not run my car up to his farm-house. I "negotiated a turn" just as the man I bought it from in New York had taught me to do; only he hadn't counted on a rail fence on one side, a rock wall just fifty feet across from it, and two stumps besides. It was almost like a maxixe, but I finally got headed toward Providence Road, down which, five miles away, Hayesboro is firmly planted in a beautiful, dreamy, vine-covered rustication.

"Oh, I wonder if it could be a devil that is possessing Sam?" I asked myself, stemming with my tongue a large tear that was taking a meandering course down my cheek because I was afraid to take either hand off the steering-gear for fear I would run into a slow, old farm horse, with a bronzed overalled driver and wagon piled high with all sorts of uninteresting crates and bales and unspeakable pigs and chickens. As I skidded past them I told myself I had more than a right to weep over Sam when I thought of the last time I had seen him before this distressing interview; the contrast was enough to cause grief.

It had happened the night after Sam's graduation in June and just the night before I had sailed with Mabel Vandyne and Miss Greenough for a wander-year in Europe. Sam was perfectly wonderful to look at with his team ribbon in the buttonhole of his dress-coat, and I was very proud of him. We were all having dinner at the Ritz with two of Sam's classmates and the father of one, Judge Vandyne, who is one of the greatest corporation lawyers in New York. He had just offered Sam a chance in his offices, together with his own son.

"You'll buck right on up through center just as you do on the gridiron, old man, to the Supreme bench before you are forty. I'm glad the governor will have you, for I'll never make it. Oh, you Samboy!" said Peter Vandyne, who was their class poet and who adored Sam from every angle—from each of which Sam reciprocated.

And all the rest raised their glasses and said: "Oh, Samboy!"

The waiters even knew who Sam was on account of the last Thanksgiving game, and beamed on him with the greatest awe and admiration. And I beamed with the rest, perhaps even more proudly. Still, that twinkle in Sam's hazel eyes ought to have made me uneasy even then. I had seen it often enough when Sam had made up his mind to things he was not talking about.

"The ladies and all of us," answered Sam to Peter's toast, as he raised his glass and set it down still full, then grinned at me as he said, so low that the others couldn't hear, "Will you meet me in Hayesboro after a year and a day, Betty?"

I don't see why I didn't understand and begin to defend Sam from himself right then instead of going carelessly and light-heartedly to Europe and letting him manage his own affairs. I didn't even write to him, except when I saw anything that interested or moved me, and then I just scribbled "remind me to tell you about this" on a post-card and sent it to him. You can seal some friends up in your heart and forget about them, and when you take them out they are perfectly fresh and good, but they may have changed flavor. That is what Sam did, and

I am not surprised that the rural flavor of what he offered me out there in dirt lane shocked me slightly. I didn't think then that I liked it and I also felt that I wished I had stayed by Sam at that wobbling period of his career; but, on the other hand, it was plainly my duty to go to Europe with Mabel and Peter Vandyne and Miss Greenough. The inclination to do two things at once is a sword that slices you in two, as the man in the Bible wanted to do to the baby to make enough of him for the two mothers; and that is the way I felt about Peter and Sam as I whirled along the road. I am afraid Sam is going to be the hardest to manage. He is harder than Peter by nature. If Sam had just taken to drink instead of farming I would have known better what to do. I reformed Peter in one night in Naples when he took too much of that queer Italian wine merely because it was his birthday. I used tears, and he said it should never happen again. I don't believe it has, or he wouldn't have got an act and a half of his "Epic of American Life" finished as he told me he had done when I dined with him in New York the night I landed. I missed Peter dreadfully when he left us in London in June, and so did Miss Greenough and Mabel, though she is his sister. We all felt that if he had been with us it wouldn't have taken us all these months of that dreadful war to get comfortably home. Peter said at the dock that he hadn't drawn a full breath since war had been declared until he got my feet off the gang-plank on to American soil. He needn't have worried quite as much as that, for we had a lovely, exciting time visiting at the Gregorys' up in Scotland while waiting for state-rooms. And it was while hearing all those Scotchmen and Englishmen talk about statesmanship and jurisprudence and international law that I realized how America would need great brains later on, more and more, as she would have to arbitrate, maybe, for the whole world.

I smiled inwardly as I listened, for didn't I know that in just a few years the nation would have Samuel Foster Crittenden to rely on? Sam is a statesman by inheritance, for he has all sorts of remarkable Tennessee ancestry back of him from Colonial times down to his father's father, who was one of the great generals of our own Civil War. And as I listened to those splendid men talk about military matters, just as Judge Crittenden had talked to Sam and me about his father, the general, ever since we were big enough to sit up and hear about it, and discuss what American brains and character could be depended upon to do, I glowed with pride and confidence in Sam. I'm glad I didn't know then about the collapsed structure of my hopes for him that Sam was even then secretly unsettling. At the thought my hand trembled on the wheel and I turned my car hastily away from two chickens and a dog in the road and my mind from the anxiety of Sam to further pleasant thoughts of Peter.

I don't believe Judge Vandyne's thoughts of Peter are as pleasant as mine, for Peter doesn't go to the office at all any more; he spends his waking moments.

at a club where players and play-writers and all men play a great deal of the time. I forget its name, but it makes the judge mad to mention it.

"The dear old governor's mind is gold-bound," said Peter, sadly, after we came away from luncheon with the judge down in Wall Street. "Why should I grub filthy money when he has extracted the bulk of it that he has? I must go forward and he must realize that he should urge me on up. I ought not to be tied down to unimportant material things. I must not be. You of all people understand me and my ambitions, Betty." As he said it he leaned toward me across the tea-table at the Astor, where we had dropped exhaustedly down to finish the discussion on life which the judge's practical tirade had evoked.

"But then, Peter, you know it was a very great thing Judge Vandyne showed his bank how to do about that international war loan. In England and Scotland they speak of him with bated breath. It was so brilliant that it saved awful complications for Belgium."

"Oh, he's the greatest ever—in all material ways," answered Peter, with hasty loyalty and some pride, "but I was speaking of those higher things, Betty, of the spirit. The things over which your soul and mine seem to draw near to each other. Betty, the second act of 'The Emergence' is almost finished, and Farrington is going to read it himself when I have it ready. He told me so at the club just yesterday. You know he awarded my junior prize for the 'Idyl.' Think of it—*Farrington!*" And Peter leaned forward and took my hand.

"Oh, Peter, I am so glad!" I said, with a catch of joy in my breath, but I drew away my hand. I knew I liked Peter in many wonderful ways, but in some others I was doubtful. I had only known Peter the three years I've been away from Hayesboro, being finished in the North, and even if I did room with his sister at the Manor on the Hudson and travel with her a year, it is not the same as being born next door to him, as in the case of Sam, for instance. But then I ought not to compare Peter and Sam. Peter is of so much finer clay than Sam. Just thinking about clay made me remember those unspeakable boots of Sam's I had encountered out on the road, and again I determinedly turned my thoughts back to that wonderful afternoon with Peter at the Astor a few short days ago. Miss Greenough kept telling Mabel and me all over Europe to look at everything as material to build nests of pleasant thoughts for our souls to rest in, as Ruskin directed in the book she had. I've made one that will last me for life of Peter, who is the most beautiful man in the whole wide world; also of the yellow shade on the Astor lamp, the fountain, and the best chicken sandwich I ever ate. It will be a warmer place to plump down in than most of the picture-galleries and cathedrals I had used for nest-construction purposes at Miss Greenough's direction.

Yes, I drew my hand away from Peter's, but a

little thing like that would never stop a poet; and before the waiter had quite swept us out with the rest of the tea paraphernalia to make way for that of dinner he had made me see that I was positively necessary to his career, especially as both his father and Mabel are so unsympathetic. It is a great happiness to a woman to feel necessary to a man, though she may not enjoy it entirely.

"Oh, I know I can write it all—all that is in my heart if I feel that it is—is for you, dearest dear Betty," was the last thing that Peter said as he put me on a train headed for the Harpeth Valley that night.

I didn't answer—I don't know that I ever did answer Peter anything, but he never noticed that when he thought of how my loving him would help out with the play.

Just here I was musing so deeply on the intricacies of love that I nearly ran over a nice, motherly old cow that had come to the middle of the road with perfectly good faith in me when she saw me coming. And as I rounded her off well to the left again my thoughts skidded back to Sam and the way he had treated me as less than a heifer calf after *I* had not seen him for a year, and *she* had just seen him that morning at feeding-time.

"Head off that saucy young cow, indeed!" I sniffed, as I ran the car into the side yard between my home and the old Crittenden house.

"I wonder if he really expected me to be waiting there in that lane for him?" I questioned myself.

And the answer I got from the six-year-old girl
that is buried alive in me was that Sam did expect
me to do as he told me, and that something serious
might happen if I didn't. As I turned Redwheels
over to old Eph, who adores it because it is the only
one he ever had his hands on, I felt a queer sinking
somewhere in the heart of that same young self.
I always had helped Sam—and suppose that unspeakable animal had got lost to him for ever just
because I hadn't done as he told me! I reached out
my hand for the runabout to start right back;
then I realized it was too late. The night had
erected a lovely spangled purple tent of twilight
over Hayesboro, and the all-evening performances
were about to begin.

Lovely women were lighting lamps and drawing
shades or meeting the masculine population at
front gates with babies in their arms or beau-
catcher curls set on their cheeks with deadly intent.
Negro cooks were hustling suppers on their smoking
stoves, and one of the doves that lives up in the vines
under the eaves of my home moaned out and was
answered by one from under the vines that grow
over the gables at the Crittendens'. I haven't felt
as lonesome as all that since the first week of Sam's
freshman year at college. As I looked across the
lilac hedge, which was just beginning to show a green
sap tint along its gray branches, I seemed to see my
poor little blue-ginghamed, pigtailed self crouched
at Judge Crittenden's feet on the front steps, sobbing
my lonely heart away while he smoked his sorrow

down with a long brier pipe, and the Byrd chirped his little three-year-old protest in concert with us both. Most eighteen-year-old men would have resented having a motherless little brother and a long-legged girl neighbor eternally at their heels, but Sam never had; or, if he did, he gently kicked the Byrd and me out of the way, and we never knew that was what he was doing. We even loved him for the kicks. Then as the tears misted across my eyes a woman with a baby in her arms came out and called in two children who were playing under the old willow-tree over by the side gate—the willow that had belonged to Sam and me—and my eyes dried themselves with indignant astonishment.

"Who are those people over at the Crittendens', mother?" I asked, in a stern voice, as I walked in and interrupted mother counting the fifteenth row on a lace mat she was making.

"Why, the Burtons bought the place from Sam after the judge's death. Don't you remember I wrote you about it, Betty dear?" she answered, with the gentle placidity with which she has always met all my tragic moments. Mother raised seven boys before she produced me, and her capacity for any sort of responsive excitement gave out long before I needed it. After her sons a woman seems to consider a daughter just a tame edition of a child. Mother has calmly crocheted herself through every soul-storm I have ever had, and she is the most dear and irresponsible parent an executive girl would wish to have leave her affairs alone. As for daddy, he has always smiled and beckoned me away from her into a corner and given me what I was making a stand for. My father loves me with such confidence that he pays no attention to me whatever except when he thinks it is about time for him to write my name on a check. His phosphate deals have made him rich in an un-Hayesboro-like way, and all the boys are in business for him in different states, except the oldest one, who is Congressman from this district, and one other who is in a Chicago bank. Yes, I know I have the most satisfactorily aloof family in the wide world. I can just go on feeding on their love and depend upon them not to interfere with any of my plans for living life. However, if anything happens to me I can be sure that their love will spring up and growl.

Now, when I stalked into the room and asked about the Crittenden home, daddy reared his head from his evening paper and immediately took notice of whatever it was in my voice that sounded as if something had hurt me.

"Daddy," I asked him, with a little gulp, "did Sam—Sam sell his ancestral home even to the third and fourth generation and go to farming just for sheer wickedness?"

"No, madam, he did not," he answered, looking at me over his glasses, and I could see a pain straighten out the corners of his mouth under his fierce white mustache. "The judge's debts made a mortgage that nicely blanketed the place, and

Sam had only to turn it over to the creditors and walk out to that little two-hundred-acre brier-patch the judge had forgot to mortgage."

"Then Sam can sell it for enough to go out and take his place in the world," I said, with the greatest relief in my voice.

"He could, but he won't," answered daddy, looking at me with keen sympathy. "I tried that out on him. Just because that brier-patch has never had a deed against it since the grant from Virginia to old Samuel Foster Crittenden of 1793 he thinks it is his sacred duty to go out and dig a hole in a hollow log for Byrd and himself and get in it to sentimentalize and starve."

"Oh, I think that is a beautiful thought about the land, and I wish I had known it earlier! But could they be really hungry—hungry, daddy?" I said, with a sudden vacant feeling just under my own ribs in the region between my heart and my stomach.

"Oh no," answered daddy, comfortably. "They both looked fat enough the last time I saw Sam coming to town in a wagon with Byrd, leading a remarkably fine Jersey calf. We'll go out in that new flying-machine you brought home with you and pull them out of their burrow some day when you get the time. Fine boy, that; and, mother, when is that two-hundred-pound black beauty in your kitchen going to have supper?"

I didn't tell daddy I had gone to the ends of the earth to hunt for Sam in less than thirty-six hours after I had landed in Hayesboro, but I went up to my room to slip into something clean and springy, walking behind a thin mist of tears of pure sentiment. That was the third time in about seven hours I had been crying over Sam Crittenden, and then I had to eat a supper of fried chicken and waffles that would have been delicious if it hadn't been flavored by restrained sobs in my throat. I was so mad at my disloyal thoughts about a beautiful character, which Sam's reverence for his ancestral land proves his to be, and so afraid of what I had done to him about the calf, and so hungry to see him, that by the time the apple-float came on the table I thought it would have to be fed to me by old Eph. Mother made it worse by remarking, as she put a lovely dab of thick cream right on top of my saucer:

"Did you hear, father, that all of Sam's cows had been sick and that he has lost his two finest calves?"

I couldn't stand any more. I gulped the cream, remarked huskily on how warm the April night was, and escaped down the front walk to the old purple lilac-bush by the gate where up to my seventh year I had always kept house with and for Sam whenever he would enter into the bonds of an imaginary marriage with me for an hour or two. Sam made a good father of a hollyhock doll family whenever he undertook the relation, and provided liberally for us all in the way of honey, locusts, and grass nuts.

"And I, maybe, let him lose the last calf he has when he is noble and poor and alone," I sobbed into my silk sleeve, which was so thin that I shivered in the cool April moonlight as I leaned against the gate and looked away out at the dim blue hills that rim the Harpeth Valley, at the foot of one of which I seemed to see Sam's and Byrd's hollow log.

"Hello, Bettykin! Out putting our hollyhock family to bed?" laughed a crisp, comforting, jolly voice right at my elbow as a big, rough hand ruffled my beautifully smoothed hair and then gave a friendly shake to my left shoulder. "How do you find all our children after a three-year foreign sojourn?"

"I told you five years ago, when I put it up on my head, to stop ruffing my hair, Sam Crittenden; and did you find that cow?" I answered, with both defiance and anxiety in my voice.

"I did," answered Sam, cheerfully, "but how did I lose you in the shuffle? I tied her up in the shack with a rope and then beat it in all these five miles, partly by foot and partly by a neighbor's buggy, to find and—er—rope you in. I am glad to see you are standing quietly at the bars waiting for me, and as soon as I've greeted your mother and Dad Hayes and got a little of the apple-float that I bet was the fatted calf they killed for your prodigal return, I'll foot it the five miles back in a relieved and contented frame of mind."

"How did you happen to let your cows get sick, Sam?" I demanded, sternly, instead of putting my arms around his neck to tell him how noble I had found out he was, and how glad I was that he had come all that way to see me, and not to be mad at me because I didn't obey him out in the lane.

"I don't know, Betty, I just don't know," answered Sam, as he lit a corn-cob pipe and leaned closer to me in a thoughtful manner. "Cows are such feminine things and so contrary. I don't know what I will do if I lose any more. I—I may get discouraged."

"Have you had a doctor?" I asked, briskly and unfeelingly, though I did take his big rough hand in my own and hold on to it with a sympathy that was not in my voice.

"No, I've sorter doctored them by a book I have. The only good veterinary doctor about here lives way over by Spring Hill, and it would take him a day to drive over and back, besides costing me about ten dollars. Still, I ought to get him. Buttercup is pretty sick," answered Sam, and I could see that his broad shoulders under his well-cut blue serge coat of last season seemed to sag with the weight of his animal responsibilities.

"I can take my car over to Spring Hill in less than an hour, get the doctor, and have you and the doctor out to those animals by ten. This moon will last all night; and you go get the apple-float from mother while I make Eph run out the car and jump into my corduroys. Come on, quick!" And as I talked I opened the gate, drew him in, and started leading him up the front walk by the sleeve of his coat.

"Not if I know myself, Betty. will I let you

undertake such a red-cross expedition as that. They'll have to wait. I came in to call on you and whisper sweet nothings to you in the parlor while you tell me—"

"Eat the float in a hurry if you want it," I interrupted him, as I deposited him beside mother, who was still sipping a last cup of coffee with her jelly-cake, and went for my room and my motor clothes.

And it was one grand dash that Redwheels and I made out Providence Road and over Paradise Ridge down to Spring Hill in less than thirty-five minutes. In the moonlight the road was like a lovely silver ribbon that we wound up on a spool under the machine, and a Southern spring breeze seemed to be helping the gasoline to waft us on more rapidly in our flight as it stung our faces with its coolness, which was scented with the sap that was just beginning to rise against bark and bud in the meadows and woods past which we sped.

"It will be great to die together, won't it, Betty?" said Sam once as Redwheels ran a few yards on two wheels, then tried the opposite two before it settled back to the prosaic though comfortable use of four as we took a flying leap across a little creek ditch.

"We can't die sentimentally; we've got to get back to those suffering cows," I answered him, firmly, as I whirled into Spring Hill and stopped Redwheels, panting and hot, in front of the dry-goods, feed, and drug store. There I knew we could find out anything we wanted to know about the whereabouts or profession of any of the fifteen hundred inhabitants of the little old hamlet which has nestled under the hills for a hundred years or more. "Ask where the cow physician lives. Quick!"

And at my urge Sam sprang out and across the old, uneven brick pavement that lay between us and the store door. Then in less than two minutes he appeared with a round, red-faced, white-headed old man who wheezed chuckles as he talked.

His fear of the car was only equaled by his fascination at the idea of the long ride in it, which would be the first motor-driven sortie he had ever made out into life.

"Air ye sure, little missie, that you can drive the contraption so as not to run away with us? Old folks is tetchy, like a basket of pullet eggs," he said, as Sam seated him in the back seat and sprang to my side.

"I wish I had a rope to tie him in," he muttered, as he sank into his seat. "If you run as you did coming, we'll sure lose him. He'll bounce like a butter-ball."

"I'm not taking any risks," I answered, and it was with greatest mildness that we sauntered up Paradise Ridge and started down the other side. And as I drove along carefully my mind began to work out into the byways of the situation. I don't see how my athletic and executive generation is going to do its appointed work in its day if we are going to go on using the same set of social conventions that tied up our mothers. As we neared

the cross-road that turned off to Sam's brier-patch I
began to wonder how long it would take me to rush
back into Hayesboro, bundle mother into Redwheels,
and get back to the cows. It was just a quarter
after nine o'clock, but I knew she would be sleepy
and would have to be forced to come with me very
gently and slowly. Still, I didn't see how I could
go on out into the woods with only Sam and the
Butterball which was wheezing out cow conversation to Sam that I was intensely interested in and
ought to have been listening to rather than wasting
force on foolish proprieties. I was about to turn
and take Sam's advice on the matter when he suddenly laid his fingers on my arm and said:

"Stop a minute, Betty. What's that roosting on
that stone wall?" And as he spoke he peered out
toward a strange, huge bird sitting by the side of the
road.

I stopped just about opposite the object and
Sam sprang out.

"You, Byrd Crittenden, where did you come
from?" I heard Sam demand of the huddled bundle
as he lifted it off the wall. It was attired in scanty
night-drawers and a short coat, and shivered as it
stood, first on one foot and then on the other.

"I ain't a-going to stay in no country with a
hoot-owl, Sam. I'm going to somewhere that a
lady lives at, too." And the manful little voice
broke as the bunch shivered up against Sam's
legs.

"Honest, Byrd, I thought you were asleep and

20

wouldn't wake up till morning. You never did before; but when I go—go gallivanting, have I got to take you or not go?" And Sam's voice was bravely jocular.

"Bring him here to me, Sam," I cried out, quickly. "Come in here with Betty, Byrd." And I cuddled his long, thin, little legs down under my lap-blanket beyond the steering-gear. "You didn't forget Betty while she was away, did you?" I asked, as we snuggled to each other and I started the motor, while Dr. Chubb chuckled and Sam still stood in the middle of the moonlit road as if uncertain what to do next.

"Yes, I forgot you," answered Byrd, candidly, though I had adored him since his birth; "but I like to go see Mother Hayes and eat jelly-cake. Can I go home with you?"

"No. I'm going as fast as I can with you to your home to keep you from freezing to death," I answered, quickly adopting this recovered old friend in the double capacity of an excuse and a chaperon. "Just sit here in the seat by me and watch me get us all back to your house in a hurry. You sit with the doctor, Sam."

"Oh no, Betty," answered Sam, quickly. "It is only a little over a mile now, and the doctor and Byrd and I can walk it all right. You come out in the morning and—"

"I'm going on with the doctor to those cows, Sam, and if you want to go with us, get in quick," I answered. in a tone of voice I have used on Sam once or twice in our lives with great effect. He hopped in and I started at top speed.

"Hic-chew! Fine goer that," wheezed the doctor, and I didn't know whether he alluded to me or Red-wheels. But there was evident relish of real pace in his voice, so I speeded up and shot away from the main road into the hard dirt lane in good style.

"I'm a bird—I'm a bird!" shouted the picked fledgling at my side as we whizzed under dark cedar boughs that waved funereal plumes over our heads, and over stumps and stones with utter disregard of the heavy new tires. One of the lessons I learned early is that men are timid of a woman's driving them in any vehicle, and I was surprised that I at last rounded the bend and drew up beside a long, low shed which Sam had calmly pointed out to me, without having had a single remonstrance from the back seat.

"Moo," came in a gentle, sad voice from the depths of the shed as we all began to disembark at the same time.

"Well, one is alive, anyway," said Sam as he set Byrd on the ground and held up his arms to me. "It's good to have you back, Betty," he whispered, in an undertone, as he turned me against his shoulder to set me down. "It 'll all go right now that you are here to—"

"Now tell us what to do, Doctor." I interrupted him determinedly, because I felt that it was not the occasion for friendly sentimentalities.

If at any time in the three years that preceded

that night I had foreseen the way I was to spend it I would have been justified in flatly refusing to carry out my horoscope. Suppose, for instance, while I was in the midst of the wonderful dinner Peter Vandyne's cousin, Count Henri de Berssan, gave me in Brussels, a week before the storm broke that carried him before cannon and bayonet, I had seen a mental picture of myself six months from that minute, out in the woods on the side of a Harpeth hill under an old cedar-pole shed with my jacket off, my embroidered blouse sleeves rolled to the shoulder, filling a tin can, which had a long spout to be poked down a cow's throat, with a vile, greasy mixture out of a black bottle, at the directions of a shirt-sleeved little man and a red-headed farmer in blue overalls, while a wisp of a boy writhed in and out and around and under a pathetic old Jersey cow, who was being rescued from the jaws of death. Now I wonder just what I would have done to escape such an experience? Slated myself for Belgian widowhood, perhaps, as a kinder fate, or stayed right there in New York to help Peter on "The Emergence." I wonder if Peter ever saw a dear, big-eyed, trustful old Jersey cow have medicine poured down her throat. It is called "drenching." I wish he could see it before he finishes that play. The sight produces a peculiar kind of emotion that might be worth recording in an all-comprehensive drama of American life. In fact, I know that what I felt at the end was worth recording in any kind of literature, by any kind of a poet—

if we were equal to it. Old Dr. Chubb leaned
breathlessly against a rough post, I staggered down
on an upturned bucket, and Sam reached out his
long, blue-overalled arms and embraced Buttercup's neck and buried his head on her patient
shoulder, just as a faint streak of April dawn showed
behind the oak-trees, for we realized then that the
dreadful cramp was gone and that she could chew
the wisp of hay offered by Byrd.

"Hic-chew! All out of the woods," wheezed
Dr. Chubb, as he looked at old Buttercup and the
two other young cows we had been working over all
night, with as fine an exaltation of achievement as
any I ever saw, not excepting that of an American
man of letters I witnessed take his degree at Oxford.

But Sam's head was still bowed on old Buttercup's back and I went and stood beside him.

"Will I ever learn how to take care the right
way of—of life?" he said under his breath, as he
stood up straight and tall with the early light
streaming over his great mop of sun-bronzed hair
and the bare breast from which his open shirt fell
away.

"I'll help you," I said, as I came still nearer and
leaned against Buttercup's warm, yellow side so
closely that she looked around from her meal from
the Byrd's hand and mooed with grateful affection
plus surprise to find us still standing by her so determinedly. "That is, if—if—I can learn myself."

"You haven't found out you are a woman yet,
have you, Betty?" answered Sam, with a laugh that

24

embarrassed me. I would have considered it ungrateful if it hadn't sounded so comfortable and warm out in the cold of the dawn—which had come before I realized that midnight had passed, about which time I had intended to go home. But how could a person feel guilty while playing Good Samaritan to a cow? I didn't.

Then, as the streak of new day widened into a soft pink flush over the tops of the bare trees that etched their fine twigs into an archaic pattern against a purple sky lit by the gorgeous flame of the morning star retreating before the coming sun, we all collected buckets and rags and bottles and sponges. In Indian file we were led by Sam around the hill, up a steep path that was bordered by coral-strung buck-bushes and rasping blackberry brush, and to his little farm-house perched on a plateau almost up to the top of the hill. It was long and low, with a wide red roof that seemed to hover in the whitewashed walls and green shutters; while white smoke from an old gray-rock, mud-daubed chimney melted away among the tree-tops into the lavender of the coming day. It looked like a great brooding white hen setting in a nest of radiant woods, and I felt like a little cold chicken as Sam led the way through the low, wide door for me to creep under the sheltering wings. In about two seconds we were all sheltered in complete comfort. At a huge fire that was a great glow of oak coals old Mammy Kitty, who had superintended Sam's birth and childhood, as well as "neighbored" mine, was gently stirring a mixture that smelled like the kind of breakfast nectar they must have in heaven, while she also balanced a steaming coffee-pot on a pair of crossed green sticks at one corner of the chimney. In the ashes I could see little mounds which I afterward found to be flaky, nutty corn-pones, and I flew to kneel at her side with my head on her gaudy neckerchief.

"Dah, dah, dah, child," she crooned, as she smiled a queer, loving, old smile that showed me how glad she was to see me, but never another word did she utter. I almost never remember hearing Mammy say an articulate word; but all children and those grown up who have any child left in their hearts can understand her croon. It is cradle music—to the initiated.

"Mammy's rheumatism is mighty bad, but she can still shake up corn ash cake and chicken hash with the best," said Sam, coming over to warm his hands and tower above us, while Byrd volunteered to lead Dr. Chubb out to what he called the wash-up bench on the back porch.

I looked up at Sam as he stood above me in a mingling of fire-glow and the early morning light with his low-beamed, deep-toned humble home as a background, and he—he loomed.

"I—I love this place," I positively gasped, as I moved still closer to Mammy and stirred the spoon in the pot of hash.

"Shelter, fire, a chicken in the pot, and a woman crouched on the hearth stirring it—what more could any man want or get, no matter how he worked?" answered Sam, as he looked down at me with the smolder in his blue-flecked hazel eyes to which Peter had once written a poem called "On the Gridiron."

"Yes, but what would you do if you didn't have Mammy?" I ventured back, as I bent across Mammy's knee and began to stir more vigorously while she shook up her coffee-pot and raked a few last coals over the cakes for their complete browning. "You always were a good provider, Sam," I added, under the excitement of the bubbling over of the coffee.

"Yes, locusts for hollyhock children and the wife of a summer day who—"

"Whew-shk! but my stomick have got a breakfas' notice," interrupted Dr. Chubb. He and the Byrd had come into the room as hungry as ravening wolves.

While Mammy stirred and shoveled off ashes I fed all three men to the point of utter repletion, feeding myself from Sam's plate as I brought the food back and forth. He didn't want me to wait on them, and I suppose that is the reason I insisted on it, and partly ate his breakfast while doing it, just as an act of defiance.

"You taught me to eat out of your hand, even when it was unspeakably dirty, and you had only saved me about two good bites and the core," I answered one of his remonstrances.

"But think of the pain it was to save even a third

of a tea-cake in your pocket when your stomach
was so near it," he answered as he finished the bottom half of a pone I had spread thick with the
juicy hash before I had greedily eaten the upper
crust.

"I'd rather eat my breakfast out of my own
plate and let ladies eat they's. Sam has to tie up
cows that eat out of other's stalls, and the old white
rooster has to be put in a coop 'cause he gobbles the
hen feed; but 'cause you are company he lets you
do it," the Byrd remarked, all in one breath between
two pieces of his pone. At which Dr. Chubb wheezed
and chuckled delightedly and Sam roared.

"Women critters ain't ever so free with vittels as
men; they have to kinder toll 'em along to nibble
feed, and life, too," remarked the doctor of distressed animals as we all rose from the table just
as the sun burst in on the situation from over
Paradise Ridge.

And while he and the Byrd went to again look
at the invalids, and Mammy Kitty removed the
dishes into a little cupboard that served as butler's
pantry and storeroom, Sam showed me the rest of
his house—which consisted of his own room, that
"leaned-to" the long living-room opposite that of
Mammy Kitty, and a back porch. That little
room made me feel queer and choky. It was neat
and poor; and a narrow, old mahogany bed, that
had always been in the Crittenden nursery, was
pushed back under the low side. It had a shelf
or two with a curtain of dark chintz under which

farm clothes hung, a gun in the corner, a jolly little wood stove, and close beside Sam's bed was the young Byrd's cot with its little pillow my mother had made for him before he was ushered into the world on the day his mother left it. I could almost see the big rough hand go out to comfort the little fledgling in the dark. I choked still further, and turned hurriedly out on to the low, wide old porch that ran all the way across the back of the house and which apparently was bath-room, refrigerator, seed-rack as to its beams, and the general depositing-place of the farm; but not before I had remarked, hanging by his door, a grass basket I had woven for Sam to bring locust pods to the hollyhock family. Then I fled, only stopping to squeeze Mammy over her dish-pan and get my hat off the cedar pegs that stuck out of the side of the old chimney to serve just such a purpose.

I found Dr. Chubb and the Byrd, who was now attired in overalls of the exact shade and cut of Sam's, standing by Redwheels with their mouths and eyes wide open in rapture.

"Well, 'fore I die I've saw a horse with steel innards and rid it," remarked the old doctor. "Machines is jest the common sense of God Almighty made up by men, 'ste'd er animals made up by Hisself. But I must git on, missie, or some critter over at Spring Hill will have a conniption and die in it fer lack of a drench or a dose."

I left Sam and the Byrd standing in the sunshine at the gate of cedar poles that Sam had set up at the entrance of his wilderness, and I don't believe I would have had the strength of character to go until I had been introduced to every stick and stone on the farm if I hadn't wanted so much to find out all about cows from Dr. Chubb. I drove slowly and extracted the whole story from his enthusiastic old mind. What I don't know about the bovine family now is not worth knowing, and I believe I would enjoy undertaking to doctor a Texas herd. We parted with vows of eternal mutual interest, and I expect to cherish that friendship. It is not every day a girl has the chance to meet and profit by such wisdom as a successful seventy-year-old veterinary surgeon is obliged to possess.

As I went up the stairs to my room I met mother coming down to her half-after-eight breakfast, and she was mildly surprised that I had not come home at a proper time and gone to bed; but when she heard that I had been with Sam's sick cows all night she was perfectly satisfied, even pleased. Mother rarely remembers that I am a girl. She has thought in masculine terms so long that it is impossible for her to get her mind to bear directly on the small feminine proprieties.

"That's right, Betty, be a doer, no matter whom you do, even if it is Sam's cow," said daddy, when I had finished my eulogy of Dr. Chubb and beautiful old Mrs. Buttercup. Then he kissed mother and me and went on down to his office, while she followed him to the gate, crocheting and quite forgetting me.

Completely exhausted, but feeling really more effective in life than I ever had before, even at the Astor tea-table (because Peter had been perfectly well and Sam's cows hadn't), I took a magazine with an entrancing portrayal of a Belgian soldier apparently eleven feet tall on the cover and went out on the side porch to sit in the cool spring sunshine and pick up the pieces of myself. When I put myself together again I found that I made something that looked like an illustration to a farm article rather than the frontispiece to an American epic. Still, if for a friend I could grasp a farm problem with that executive enthusiasm, had I any reason to doubt that I would have any trouble in helping along an epic of American life? I decided that I would not, and settled down to find out about the eleven-foot Belgian before I crept off for a nap, when an interruption came and I had to prop my eyes open. It was Eph with a letter and the information that Redwheels had shed a bolt in its flight last night. I settled the bolt question with a quarter and turned to the letter. It was from Peter, and I knew by the amount of ink splashed all over the envelope that it must contain a high explosive splashed on the inside.

Peter Vandyne really is a wonderful man, and he will enrich American letters greatly after he has had time to live a lot of the things he has planned to write. Farrington, the great producer and dramatist, had read the first act of his epic and said good things about it. Farrington is not a friend of

Peter's sister, Mabel, nor does he own or want to buy any of Judge Vandyne's stock in railroads or things. He's just really the dean of the American stage. Could anybody blame Peter if he had used ten pounds of paper, if paper comes by the pound, and a quart of ink telling about it? But he didn't; about five of the seven pages were all about me and Farrington. I never was so astonished. The morning I got home I had written Peter about how all my friends had been glad to see me, and the way the different ones had shown it, and Peter had read that part to Mr. Farrington and he had said that Peter ought to get me to supply some of the human comedy that Peter's play lacked. Peter knows so much about life from his literary researches that it goes off and hides from him when he sets out in search for it, and I understood immediately what the great dramatist meant, though Peter probably did not.

So weave some of your heart spells for me, dearest dear Betty [Peter wrote]. I am sending you the manuscript of Act I and part of Act II, and I know you will read them carefully and let me know fully what you think of them. Criticize them from your splendid human viewpoint. The dear old governor has been rather hard on me of late, and I may have to go into the office yet. Death! Help, rescue me, dear, for to put a play across will be my salvation from his prejudices. I must do it this summer, and then—then by the new year perhaps I can lay the gems of success at your feet. May I come down and talk to you soon about it all? No one knows what's in my heart but you, my own Betty. May I come?

PETER.

I was extremely happy and excited over the poetical way in which Peter was calling on my common sense to help him in his crisis, but I felt weighted down with the responsibility. Yes, I understood the great Farrington. He felt as I did—that Peter's genius needed to see and help old Dr. Chubb drench Buttercup with a can of condition-mixture. Now, could I supply all that, or enough of it to keep Peter from being murdered in his father's office? The inky bundle at my side began to look as if it weighed a ton, but my loyalty and affection for Peter made me know that I must put my back to the burden and raise it somehow. If it had been a simple burden, like three sick cows, it would have been easier to take upon my shoulders. Then suddenly, as I was about to be in a panic about it all, the thought of the cows reminded me of Sam, and immediately, in my mind, I shared the weight of the manuscript with him and began to breathe easier. The way Sam and Peter love each other inspires positive awe in my heart, though Mabel says it is provoking when they go off to their fraternity fishing-camp for week-ends instead of coming to her delightful over-Sunday parties out on Long Island. Judge Vandyne feels as I do about it, and he loves Sam as much as Peter does, though I don't believe that he has any deeper affection for Peter than Sam has. I've been intending to read up about David and Jonathan, but I feel sure, from dim memories, that their histories about describe Peter and Sam. I couldn't for the life of me see why any woman should resent "a love that passes the love of" her, and I am sure she wouldn't if one of them was a poet born to enlighten the world. Yes, I breathed easier at the thought of Sam's affection for Peter, and went back to the case of the giant Belgian, though I don't think the artist quite intended him to be taken that way.

Just as I had turned the front page I was interrupted by Clyde Tolbot, who came whistling down the street and broke out all over with smiles when he saw me out sunning myself.

"Gee! Betty, but it is good to see you at home!" he said.

They were almost the exact words Sam had used, but they sounded different. The sound is about all that is different in any of the things men say to girls when they like them a lot. Tolly and I are very appreciative of each other, and always have been.

"You are going to settle down and have a royal good time, aren't you, Betty? I learned a new foxtrot up in Louisville last week I'm dying to teach you, and now that Sue Bankhead has got a great big dance machine we can fox almost every night. Will you come with me this evening?"

"I wish I could, Tolly," I said, with utter sincerity, for Tolly is the very best dancer in the Harpeth Valley, not excepting Tom Pollard over at Hillsboro. "But, Tolly, I must give up all thought of social pleasures for a time." I spoke with a dignified reserve that fitted the spirit that I ought to have when undertaking a great responsibility, though I did want to dance. "I have some hard mental work to do."

"Well, blast old Hayesboro for a sad hole! You are going to go in for brain athletics, Sam Crittenden for farmer heroics, and the only movie that has peeped into town is going to be closed because it ran a Latin Quarter film the afternoon the ladies stopped in from the United Charities sewing circle, expecting a Cuban missionary thriller. I might as well have my left foot amputated, it itches so for good dancing." Tolly was so furious that I was positively sorry for him, and to comfort and calm him I told him all about Peter's letter and the play, and the way I had to read and criticize and help. He sniffed at the idea of Peter, but the dramatist impressed him slightly.

"Say, that old boy is the real thing, Betty, child. He's the sure win-out on Broadway. But how long will it take you to write that play for your molly-coddle poet? You can get through with it before the Country Club gets going good, can't you? We've had a new floor in the dancing-pavilion built, and the directors ordered a foxy music machine last night."

"Oh yes, I ought to be able to tell Peter all I know in two and a half months," I answered, ignoring Tolly's disrespect for my poet friend.

"And a lot you don't know," Tolly added, with the candor of real affection. "I wish Sam, the old calf, could be weaned from his cows and take the position your dad is offering him at the Phosphate Works, so he would be able to shake a foot occasionally. Can't you handle him a bit, Betty? It's as if he just came out and looked at life and then dived back in a hollow log."

"I—I don't know," I answered, doubtfully. A pang shot through me at the thought of any one extracting Sam from that wonderful retreat in the woods, but then also this news of the honors that were coming to Peter made me long to have Samuel Foster Crittenden come forth and take his place in the world beside his friends. Sam, I felt sure, was made to shine, not to have his light hid under a farm basket. Why, even Tolly, there beside me on the steps, was the head of the new Electric Light Company that Hayesboro has had a little over a year. He did it all himself, though he had failed to pass his college examinations when he went up for them with Sam.

"I'm proud of the way you've been doing things, Tolly," I added, warmly, putting my thoughts of Sam away where I keep them when I'm not using them.

"Oh, I'm just an old money-grubber and nobody's genius child, but I'll rustle the gold boys to get up to New York to see your play, Betty, and send you a wagon-load of florist's spinach on the first night," answered Tolly, beaming at my words of praise.

"Oh, Tolly, please don't think I'm going to write a play," I answered, quickly. "I'm—well, I'm just going to tell Peter a whole lot of useful things I find out about life. You see, Tolly, Peter's father has so many millions of dollars that it has been almost impossible for Peter to climb over them into real life as we have. I have to do it for him. Please pity Peter, Tolly, and tell me what you think would be nice in his play if you find anything."

"Well—er—well, I have right in stock at present a little love-interest tale I could unfold to you, Betty, about— Help! There comes the gentle child Edith up the street now. I must go. I am too coarse-grained for association with her." And before I could stop him he was gone through the house and out the back way. That is the way it always is with Tolly and Edith, either they are inseparable or entirely separate. They can't seem to be co-existent citizens, and they have been fighting this way since they both had on rompers. I wondered what Tolly had been doing now.

"Clyde Tolbot needn't have gone just because I came. I can endure him when I have other people to help me," said Edith, as she kissed me and sat down sadly. She is always sad when Tolly has been sinful.

"What has Tolly been doing now?" I asked her, as I put that fascinating Belgian face down on the floor and ruthlessly sat upon him, for the step was getting cold, though the sun was delicious and had drawn out a nice old bumblebee from his winter quarters to scout about the budding honeysuckle over our heads.

"I am so hurt that I wouldn't tell anybody about it but you, dear, but last night as he walked home with me, after we had been dancing down at Sue's to the new phonograph, he—he put his arm almost around me and I think—I think he was going to kiss me if I hadn't prevented him—that is, he did kiss my hair—I think." Edith is the pale-nun type, and I wish she could have seen how lovely she was with the blush that even the failure of Tolly to kiss her brought up under her deep-blue eyes. Edith didn't get any farther north to school than Louisville, and her maiden aunt, Miss Editha Shelby Morris Carruthers, brought her up perfectly beautifully. I didn't know how to comfort her because I had been two years at the Manor on the Hudson and then a year in Europe, and, though nobody ever has directly kissed me, a girl's hand and hair don't seem to count out in the world.

To take Edith's mind off Tolly's perfidy I told her about the play, and she was as impressed as anybody could wish her to be, and promised to stand by me and make people understand why I couldn't dance and picnic like other people because of this great work I had to do for a dear friend. I told her not to tell anybody but Sue, and she went home completely comforted by her friendly interest in Peter and me. In fact, she really adored the idea of helping me help Peter, and seemed to forget her anger at Tolly with a beautiful spirit.

About that time Eph solemnly called me in to lunch. Eph is a nice, jolly old negro until he gets a

white linen jacket and apron on, and then he turns
into a black mummy. I think it is because I used
to want to talk to him at the table when I still sat
in a high chair. I don't believe he has any confidence
in my discretion even now, and that is why he seats
me with such a grand and forbidding display of
ceremony.

"Betty dear," said mother, after Eph had served
her chicken soup and passed her the beaten biscuits, "I found an old note-book of my mother's that
has all the wonderful things she did to the negroes
and other live stock on her farm out in Harpeth
Valley. You know she ran the whole thousand
acres herself after father's death in her twenty-
seventh year, and she was a wonderful woman,
though she did have three girls and only one son.
There is a section of her notes devoted to cows and
their diseases, and Sam might be interested to hear
how she managed them so that even then her cows
sold for enormous sums. Suppose you look over it
and tell him about it."

"Oh, I will. Thank you, mother!" I answered,
as I took three little brown biscuits, to Eph's affectionate delight, and also as a shock to his proprieties.

I had planned to open the bundle and begin my
work for Peter right after dinner, but I sat down
and devoured whole that note-book of my maternal
ancestor's. I never was so thrilled over anything,
and the chapter on gardening really reads like a
beautiful idyl of summer. It changed my entire
nature. As I read I glowed to think that I could go

right to Sam's wilderness and try it all out. I
didn't own any land, and it might take a little time
to force daddy to buy me some, and the planting
season and fever were upon me. There is a wide
plateau to the south of Sam's living-room, and I
had in my mind cleared it of bushes, enriched it
with all the wonderful things grandmother had
directed, beginning with beautiful dead leaves, and
I was planting out the row of great blush peonies
in my mind as I intended to plant it in Sam's garden
when the tall old clock in the hall toned out four long
strokes. Then I remembered that I wanted to go
down to the post-office to get my mail and to see
everybody and hear the news. So with the greatest
reluctance I tucked the garden idyl in the old desk
which had been that very Grandmother Nelson's,
and heaved Peter's heavy manuscript in on top
of it.

No mass-meeting, no picnic, and no function out
in the great world, even New-Year's reception at
the White House or afternoon tea at the Plaza,
could be half the fun that going to the Hayesboro
post-office for the afternoon mail is. I think the
distinct flavor is imparted by the fact that all our
forefathers and foremothers have done it before us.
The Hayesboro resurrection will be held right there,
I feel sure.

And if mail-time is fun usually, it is great when all
the news is about you and your friends all swarm
around you with interest. Everybody had heard
about Peter and his play, though neither Edith nor

Tolly thought they had told, and that he was soon coming down to visit me, and, of course, that meant to visit all of Hayesboro. Miss Henrietta Spain, who teaches literature from spelling to the English poets, in the Hayesboro Academy, had read Peter's new poem—the one the *Literary Opinion* had copied last month—and she was pink with excitement over the prospect of having such a genius in our midst.

"Look out that you don't get put in the play on the other side of the footlights, Hayes," said the mayor, slapping daddy on the back. "Be careful how you have a poet sitting around your house."

"The South has long waited to have a genius come down and write a fitting epic about her Homeric drama of Civil War, Elizabeth," said old Colonel Menefee. "Let your young friend come, and I can give him material, beginning with that Bedford Forest charge just before Chickamauga that—"

"And just remember," interrupted Mrs. Winston Polk, "how Elizabeth's mother, Betty's own Grandmother Nelson, rode fifty miles and back in twenty-four hours to get Morgan to send wagons for her barnful of corn to feed his soldiers, though she and her negroes were dependent on what she could grow between then and frost. She never faltered, but—"

"The Nashville and Louisville papers all wrote up the way Clyde Tolbot swam Salt River and stopped the L. & N. express from going down in the cut during the storm last year," Edith hastened to say when Mrs. Polk's breath had given out. Tolly's

ugly good face was beautiful to see when she spoke
of him thus, though Edith didn't notice it.

When you start a Harpeth Valley town to telling
how wonderful it is to the third and fourth generation
back, it is like a seething torrent and can go on for
ever. I glowed to think of all the wonderful things
I could write Peter, and we all started home from
the post-office as late as supper hour would admit.

After I got home, escorted by the reunited Edith
and Tolly, as well as by Billy Robertson, who wants
to be Peter's hero, though he wasn't directly saying
so, I sat down determinedly to write to Peter at
inspiring length and make him feel how I valued his
confidence in me, also to mention the war drama.
Just then I raised my eyes and that wonderful note-
book had pushed a corner of itself out of the desk
from under the manuscript. I couldn't use my
mind advising between a modern epic and a war
drama while it was plowed up ready for peonies, so
I decided to wait and ask Sam's advice about advising Peter, and I read the rest of the peony pages
in comfort. Right then, too, I made up my mind
that I was going to get ground bone to plant at the
roots of all the peonies if I had to use my own
skeleton to do it and would only see them bloom
with astral eyes.

I was still reading when the supper-bell rang, and
was only interested in reminiscences of Grandmother Nelson during the meal.

"No, ma'am, Miss Caroline, you got it wrong.
Ole Mis' didn't divide clover pinks 'cepting every

third year 'stid of second. *Hers* bloomed, they did," Eph interrupted mother to say, indulging in perhaps his first speech while waiting on the table during the long and honorable life as a butler which that grandmother had started at his sixth year. He then retired in the blackest consternation, and his yellow granddaughter, the house-girl, brought in the wine-jelly.

One thing is certain—I must contrive some way to get Sam back and forth to me from The Briers in less time than it takes him to walk five miles. He has got just one old roan plow mare and he won't ride her after he has worked her all day, and I am afraid it won't do for me to go after him with Redwheels every time I want him. I can go about two-thirds of the time, but he must be allowed some liberty about expressing his desire for my company. Of course a tactful woman can go nine-tenths of the way in all things to meet a man she likes, and he'll think she hasn't even started from home; but she ought to be honorable enough not to do it at that rate. I believe in liberty for men as well as women.

Still, I can't express the strain it was on me to wait until after eight o'clock for Sam with Grandmother Nelson's farm-book on my knee, and I don't want to do it ever again, especially if the Byrd or Mammy or the cows or any of the other live stock might be sick. I felt that it must be midnight before I got Sam seated by me on the deep old mahogany sofa in front of one nice April blaze in behind the brass fender, and under another from

Tolly's power-house. He was pretty tired, as he had been up since daylight, but the cows were all right and on feed again, Mammy wasn't any stiffer than usual, and he had promised the Byrd the first chicken that the old Dominicker hatched out to stay at home and let him come to see me. Mammy had sent me five fresh eggs, and Sam presented them with a queer pod of little round black seeds, and a smile that wouldn't look me in the face.

"Hollyhocks! I climbed over the Johnson fence about two miles from town and stole them for you," he said, as he squirmed around from me and picked a brown burr off the leg of his trousers.

"Aren't they sweeties?" I exclaimed, not noticing his entirely unnecessary bashfulness. "And that is just what I want to talk to you about." With which I produced my ancestral treasure, and with our heads close together we dove into it, didn't come up until after ten o'clock, and then were breathless.

"Oh, Sam, can I do all these things out at your farm?" I exclaimed, and I fairly clung against his shoulder while his strong, rough hand folded over mine as the husk did over the hollyhock seeds I had been holding warm and moist in my palm.

"All of them, and then some, Betty," he answered, blowing away a wisp of my hair that he had again roughed up instead of shaking hands in greeting, despite my reproof. "I'll plow up that southern plot for you just after daylight to-morrow, and every minute I can take from grubbing at the things I have to work to make the eats for all of us I'll put in on the posy-garden for you."

"I'm much obliged to you for the plowing, but I'll be out at about nine o'clock and I'll bring my own spade and hoe and rake and things. I think I'll take those two young white lilacs that are crowded over by the fence in the front yard to start the garden. Don't you think lilacs would be a lovely corner for a garden like my grandmother's, Sam?"

"I—I think it would be nice to—plant the holly-hock seeds you have in your hand the first thing, Betty," answered Sam, with the gridiron smolder in his eyes which snapped up into a twinkle as he added, "Could you help me set onions for a few hours later on?"

"Oh, I'd adore it!" I answered, enthusiastically. "Of course, I mean to help plant all the eat things, too. I may like them best. Let's see what grand-mother says about onions." And I began to ruffle back the pages of the book that Sam held in both his hands for me.

"Good gracious! Betty, couldn't the old lady write!" exclaimed Sam, a half-hour later, after we had finished with onions and many other profitable vegetables. "Why, that description of her hog's dying with cholera and the rescue reads like a—a Greek tragedy in its simplicity."

"Oh, Sam," I exclaimed in dismay, "that re-minds me, I forgot to tell you about the play, and now you ought to go home, with all those five miles to walk and plowing to do at daylight."

"Play? What play? Won't it keep?" asked Sam, as he rose and reached for his hat on the table. "Let's enjoy this last ten minutes before my hike, down at the gate."

"Oh no, it won't keep, and I don't know exactly what I will do about it and the garden. Here's Peter's letter; read it for yourself," I wailed, as I drew the splashed letter out from the ruffle in the front of my dress where I had stuck it for safe keeping, and handed it to Sam. If I hadn't been so distressed by the collision of the play and the garden in my heart I never would have been so dishonorable as to let Sam read the last paragraph in Peter's letter, which was more affectionate than I felt was really right for Peter to write me, even after the Astor tea-party, and which had troubled me faintly until I had forgotten about it in my excitement about Farrington and the play. I saw Sam's hand shake as he read that last page, and he held it away from me and finished it, as I remembered and gasped and reached for it.

"Good old Pete," said Sam, in a voice that shook as his hand did while he handed me back the letter. "It is a great chance for him, and if you can help you'll have to go to it, Betty. Pete only needs ballast, and you are it—he seems to think."

"But how will I find time enough from making our garden to help make his play?" I asked as I rose and clung to his sleeve as I had done in all serious moments of my life, even when his coat-sleeve had

46

been that of a roundabout jacket. My heart was weak and jumpy as I asked the question.

"Betty," said Sam, gently, lifting my hand from his arm into his for a second and then handing it firmly back to me, "that garden was just a dream you and I have been having this evening. It can't be. Don't you see, dear, I am in a hard hand-to-hand struggle with my land, which is all I possess, for—for bread for myself and the kiddie, and I—I can't have a woman's flower-garden. It looks as if you and old Petie can do a real literary stunt together. Just get at it, and God bless you both. Good night now; I must sprint." And as he spoke he was through one of the long windows and out on the front porch in the moonlight.

"Oh, wait, Sam, wait!" I gasped, as I flew after him and clung to him determinedly.

"Well," he said, patiently, as he stood on the step below me and turned his bronze head away from me out toward his dim hills sleeping in the soft mystery of the moonlight.

"I will, Sam, I *will* have that garden," I said, with the same angry determination in my voice I had used when I had clung to him and kicked and fought to go to places with him when he didn't want me, and when my skirts were several inches above my bare knees and his feet were scratched and innocent of shoes.

"Betty," said Sam, as he shook me away from him and then took my shoulders under their thin covering of chiffon in his plow-calloused, big, warm

47

hands, "forget it! There are lots of dream gardens out in the world you can play in when you have time away from the bright lights. Everybody grows 'em without a lick of work. I have to work mine or starve. Good night!" Then with a rough of my hair down across my eyes he was out in the moonlit road, running away from me to his hollow log in a way he had never done before, no matter how I had tagged him.

I ran as far as the gate to watch him out of sight, and then I put my head down against the tall old post that had been one of Sam's perches when he wanted to climb away from me in former years, and sobbed and sobbed. I had never expected Sam to cast me off.

Girls' hearts are covered all over with little thin crystallizations of affection, and men ought to be very careful not to smash any of them with their superior strength. Sam had hurt me so that I didn't even dare think about it. I knew he was poor, and I hadn't expected him to plow and plant things for me while I went about in a picture-hat snipping them with garden scissors. I had asked him to let me set onions and weed beans and drop peas and corn for him and share his poverty and hard work as a true friend, and he had shut his cedar-pole gate in my face and heart. And I didn't understand why. I tried to think it was his affection for Peter that made him thus rudely switch my mind from him and his garden to Peter and his need of me, which Sam may have thought was greater than the need of his onions and turnip salad; but I don't see how Sam could have construed cruelty to me as generosity to Peter.

"Please God," I prayed out into the everlasting hills toward which Sam was running away from me and from which I had heard intoned "cometh help," "give me dirt to work in somewhere except in just a yard if I can't have Sam's. Help me to get somebody to help me to raise things for people to eat and milk, as well as to inspire a play. I'll do both things, but I must have earth with rotted leaves in it. Amen."

Then I went to bed heartbroken for life, and my sad eyes closed on the little glimpse which my window framed of Old Harpeth, the tallest hill in Paradise Ridge, while my hand still folded in the moist hollyhock seeds.

II

THE BOOK OF SHELTER

PETER'S play is remarkable; it really is. He has collected all the great and wonderful things that life in America contains and put them together in a way that reads as if Edgar Allan Poe had helped Henry James to construct it, though they had forgotten to ask Mark Twain to dinner and had never heard of John Burroughs. I felt when I got through the first act as if I had been living for a week shut into an old Gothic cathedral aisle decorated by marble-carved inspired words, and I was both cold and hungry. The more I read of Peter's play the more congenial I felt with Farrington. I had enough education to see that it was a genuine literary achievement, but I had heart enough to know that something had to be done to rescue all his characters from the arctic region. Could I do it single-handed even for a person I cared as much for as I did for Peter? I decided that I could not, and that the only way I could prove my loyalty and affection for Peter was to abase myself before Sam Crittenden and his cruelty to me, and get his help. Only for Peter would I have done such a thing, which in the end I didn't have to do at all.

Since the night Sam refused me the use of his farm and put me out of his life for ever I had not seen him until by his own intention. Or maybe it was Tolly's.

"See here, Betty, what you need is a good fox or tango and you had better come to it up at Sue's to-night."

Tolly had broken in upon my despairing meditations over the way in which Peter's hero talks wicked business and congested charity to the poor little heroine in the very first act while she is full of a beautiful affection Peter didn't seem to see, and ready to pour it forth to the hero before he started out on a long life mission. Maybe it was sorrowing with her at being thus suppressed by everybody that made me write her case to Peter with such fervor. I had just finished the letter when Tolly came to my rescue with the offer of a nice warm dance to nourish me up.

"Don't make me kidnap you, Betty; go fluff and rose up a bit," he commanded, as he seated himself on the front steps with a determination which was as business-like as his management of the Electric Light Company.

"I think I had better go to Sue's to thaw out some of my loneliness over this play," I answered him as I looked up with desperation and a smudge on my face. Then I went to my room and left Tolly alone with Peter's poor little heroine.

"Say, tell the poet to get the man with the dinner-pail who is eating hunk sandwiches at lunch-time on the pavement in front of any construction job in New York to tell him what he did and said to his girl at the firemen's ball the night before, and then translate it into some of this first-class poetry. That 'll be a great play," said Tolly, as I came down-stairs just as he had turned page twenty-five of Peter's manuscript. Tolly's coarseness doesn't affect me as it does Edith because there is always so much point to it.

"You don't quite understand Peter and his play, Tolly, dear," I said, with dignity, though I felt exactly the same way about it and hadn't known how to express it in human interest terms as well as Tolly.

"I sure don't," answered Tolly, cheerfully, and not at all as if I had put him in his place in regard to his criticism of our epic. "Come on; let's hurry. Everybody is waiting for us."

It was good to be in a buzz of girls and men once more for the first time in two weeks since I settled down to do my worst or best by Peter, with my Grandmother Nelson's garden-book locked up in the preserve-closet down in the darkest corner of the cellar, and Sam lost in the fastness of The Briers.

Everybody wanted to dance with me at the same time, and the girls kissed me into a lovely, warm cheerfulness. The girls in Hayesboro are the sustaining kind of friends, like pound-cake, sweetened and beautifully frosted.

"Has he consented to let the hero kiss the poor thing's hand before he goes to fight the case of the miners?" Julia whispered, warmly, as she took a few tango steps with me in her arms before Billy Robertson claimed her and Tolly picked me up to juggle with me in his new Kentucky version of the fox-trot.

"I'm expecting a letter to-morrow," I answered her as Tolly slid me away three steps, skidded two, and slid back four. And then, having begun, I danced; all of me danced; even my heart, which had started out as heavy as lead, got into the feather class before I went around the room three times. It is strange how even great responsibilities melt away before dance music like icicles on the southern side of the house. It was in a perfectly melted condition that I at last dropped from Tolly's grasp into a pair of new arms which cradled me against a broad breast with such gentleness that I might have thought it was mother come to the dance if I hadn't caught a whiff of cedar woodsiness when I turned my nose into a miniature brier-patch of blue-berried cedar in the buttonhole of the coat against which my face was pressed as my feet caught step with a pair of smart shoes bearing a smear of moss loam on one side.

"Sam!" I gasped, with emotional indignation that had a decided trace of joy.

"Yes, I feel that way, too," answered Sam, roughing my hair slightly with his chin as both his hands were employed holding me to him while we slid and skidded and slid again.

5   53

"I don't forgive you; I never shall," I said, haughtily, as I drew away from him the fraction of an inch that came very near making us collide with Sue and Billy, who were dancing wildly, but in perfect accord.

"You'll have to when you hear the worst," answered Sam, as he firmly pressed my shoulder into his while he manœuvered me first past Edith and Tolly and then across right in front of Pink Herriford, who weighs all of two hundred, dancing with Julia Buford, who must tip the scales at one hundred and sixty. It was a hairbreadth rapture of escape.

"Is anything the matter with the cows or anybody else?" I demanded, anxiously, from his shoulder.

"Worse!"

"Oh, Sam, has anything died at The Briers?"

"Worse," he answered again, while he defied Tolly with a double cross and then took a chance with Pink and Julia as I pressed him closer with my arms and my questions.

"Dance me out on the porch through the window and tell me, Sam," I demanded.

"Not when this music and Julia and Pink hold out like that, Bettykin. It 'll be bad enough when you do hear it," answered Sam, laughing down at me with the same wide-mouthed smile he had always used on me when holding something over my head and making me reach up for it. "Besides, it has been two whole weeks since I've—had you," he added, and again his strong arms cradled as well as guided.

Getting back into some people's atmosphere is like recovering the use of a lung a person had temporarily lost; breathing improves. I've always breathed easily in Sam's friendship. That was why I could dance with him as I did even up to the last bar of the music. Then he swung me out through one of the long windows on to the porch under the dusky spring starlight.

"I hate to tell you, Betty, though I have walked a five-mile blister on my left heel in these dancing-shoes just to break the news to you," Sam answered my repeated demand to be told his "worse."

"Oh, Sam, a real blister?" I exclaimed, losing sight of the threatened catastrophe at the thought of his blistered heel. I knew how tender Sam's feet were, for I had doctored them since infancy. I used to pay tribute in the form of apples and tea-cakes for the privilege of binding up his ten and twelve year old wounded toes, and I suppose I hadn't really got over my liking for thus operating.

"Oh, not all from the walk," answered Sam, as he smiled down on me consolingly. "I've got a brand-new mule and I nearly plowed him and myself to death to-day. I don't seem to be well heeled enough to plow and dance both."

"What did you plow, Sam?" I came close up to his shoulder so that the bit of woods in his button-hole grazed my cheek as my head drooped with an embarrassed hope.

"I plowed for the early potatoes on the south slope and—and—"

"And what?"

"I'm thinking of growing a crop of—hollyhocks, if I get time to plant 'em."

"Where did you plow, Sam?"

"In spots all over the place."

"Where?"

"Well, then, about a hundred feet south by southwest from my door-step, if you must have it. Great sakes! do you think this heel is going to swell, Betty, from your deep experience?"

"I—I'm so happy, Sam," I faltered, with more emotion than I knew Sam liked, but I think all apologies ought to be met enthusiastically at the front gate, whether they intended to come in or not.

"Well, I'm not — I'm blistered." He again plaintively referred to his sufferings which I had forgotten in my joy at having him back in the bonds of friendship, even if slightly damaged.

"Come over home with me and I'll plaster it so it won't break or swell. You know I know how," I answered, eagerly.

"Cold cream and an old handkerchief like you used to keep. Um — um! the thought is good, Betty," he answered, as he stood on his left foot for a second and then lifted it as if he were a huge crane.

"Come, now, so I can get the cream before mother goes to bed," I said, with energy; and I led him, faintly remonstrating, through the Bankhead back gate that opens opposite ours.

Mother was glad to see Sam, heel and all, and

sympathetically supplied the cream and handkerchief and a needle and thread without laying down the mat she was putting in a difficult hundred-and-fifty round on. Mother is so used to Sam that she forgets that he is not her fifth or sixth son, and she treats him accordingly. After she had given us all the surgical necessities she retired into the living-room by the lamp to put her mind entirely on the mat, in perfect confidence that I could do the right thing by my wounded neighbor. And I did.

First, as I had always done, I bathed Sam's great big pink-and-white foot in hot water and then in cold, sitting on the floor with a bath-towel in my lap to get at it while Sam wriggled and squirmed at both hot and cold just as he had always done.

"Go on, boil me," he said, as I poured the last flash of heat from the tea-kettle on the floor beside me.

"Now a frost," he groaned, as I dashed ice-water out of a pitcher on the blister and lifted the foot into my lap on the bath-towel.

"If you touch the bottom of my foot I'll yell 'murder,'" he said as I began to pat all around the blister in the gentlest and most considerate manner possible. I knew he meant what he said, so I was careful as I wound and clipped and sewed.

"I never fixed as nice a one as that for you before," I said, with pride, as he drew on his silk sock with its huge hole over as neat a bandage as it was possible for human hands to accomplish. "I love to tie you up, Sam."

"Thank you, and I return the compliment," answered Sam, both smouldering and smiling down at me as if he were saying something to tease me. "And now as a reward for your kindness I am going to knock you down with some news." And as he spoke we went on out to the porch, Sam walking like a new man.

"Oh, the 'worse' thing! I had forgotten about that. Tell me, Sam," I answered, as I leaned against one of the pillars of the porch and he seated himself on the railing beside me.

"Well," said Sam, slowly, "this is not worse for you, just for me; that is, at the present speaking, with nothing but the hay-loft handy. I don't know just how I'll manage."

"What?"

"Pete," answered Sam.

"What about Peter? Oh, Sam, Peter isn't ill, is he?" And I reached out and clutched Sam's arm frantically. It takes alarm to test the depths of one's affection for a friend. I found mine for Peter deeper than I knew. If anything had happened, Sam would know it first. "Don't be cruel to me, Sam." And I shook his arm.

"Forgive me, Betty," said Sam, quickly. "Pete's all right and he'll be here to demonstrate it to you just as soon as I can get a stall built for him out at The Briers."

"At The Briers? Peter?" I gasped.

"Even at that humble abode, Betty, whose latch-string is always out to friends," answered Sam.

And I felt his arm stiffen under my fingers in a way for which I could see no reason.

"Just as I was going to begin my garden," I wailed. And Sam's stiff arm limbered again and made a motion toward my hair that I dodged. "What does he want?"

"Direct life. I can give it to him," answered Sam. "At least that is what he asked for in his letter to me. I don't know what he will request in the one I wager you get by the morning mail."

"Why, I had been writing him all that he needed of that, and we are going to be so busy gardening, how can we help him live it also? Peter does require so much affectionate attention." I positively wailed this to Sam, in the most ungenerous spirit.

"Betty dear," said Sam, gently, as he puffed at a little brier which he had substituted for the adorable cob on account of the formality of Sue's dance, which we could hear going on comfortably without us, beyond the privet hedge whose buds were just beginning to give forth a delicious tang, "Peter is a great, queer kind of sensitive plant that it may be we will have to help cultivate. You know that for several years his poems have really got across in great style with the writing world, and I'm proud of him and—I—I—well, I love him. Suppose, just suppose, dear, that Keats had had a great hulking farmer like me to stand by. Don't you think that maybe the world would have had some grown-man stuff from him that would have counted? I always have thought of that when I looked at old Pete and

59

promised myself to back him up with my brawn and nerve when he needed it. Why, in the '13 game it was Pete's flaming face up on the corner of the stadium that put the ginger in me to carry across as I did. Yes, I am going to put Pete's hand to my plow and his legs under old Buttercup at milking-time if it kills us both, if that is what he needs or you have made him think he needs."

"Oh, Sam, I'm ashamed! I'm ashamed of not wanting precious Peter in my garden. He can have half of all of it. You know I love him dearly. I'll work all day with him and attend to all his blisters and get everybody to give him work and help him."

"Well, I don't believe I'd do all that to him, Betty," answered Sam, with a laugh. Then his eyes glinted past mine for a second. "And say, Betty, you know my blisters are kind of—kind of old friends to you; Pete's might not have so many —many landmarks for you to work by," he added, as he knocked the ashes carefully out of the brier and picked up his hat. "Let's go for one fox, and then I'll trot on out to my patch."

"I'll get Tolly to run you out in Redwheels while I do my promised dances, and then I'll be out early in the morning to help plan about Peter. And —and, Sam, do you want to—to give me that garden?"

"Everything that is is yours, Bettykin," he answered as we went down the steps out on to the springy greening grass and across to the back gate.

Some friends taste like bread and butter and peach preserves. Sam does and he's a peach.

When I got back to the Bankheads' everybody was wondering where we had been, and as Sam and Tolly got right off in the car without answering any questions, I was left to explain about Sam's foot and Peter. I paid no attention at all to Billy Robertson when he said his foot was blistered, too; but I told them how beautiful Peter was, and how distinguished, and all about the poor young Keats that most of them hadn't grieved over since their Junior years at school, telling it all in such an eloquent way that Julia's great blue eyes filled with tears, and I saw I could depend on her to be nice to our friend.

"I knew most poets were kind of calves, but I didn't know they had to milk their poetry out of a genuine cow," said Pink, with a vulgar attempt to be funny, at which nobody laughed, not even Julia, and she is almost too tall and big to dance with anybody but Pink. She and Edith and Sue and I forgot to save him the dances we had promised him; and he had to dance with other girls he didn't like so much, until we all went home in time to meet the sun coming down over Paradise Ridge with his dinner-pail.

Then for five days it rained—heavy, determined, soggy drops; but the next morning introduced one of those wily, flirtatious days that come along about the last week in April in Tennessee. I awoke to the sound of sobbing wind and weeping clouds in

61

which I had no confidence, and succeeded in convincing mother that it would be a beautiful day for me to go out to see Sam and Byrd and Mammy. She sent Byrd half a jelly-cake and a bag of bananas, and I got a jar of jam for him when I went down in the cellar to exhume Grandmother Nelson's garden-book. A bottle went to Mammy, which I suspect of being a kind of liniment that mother had to learn to make on account of the number of the boys and their bruises.

Eph was a tragedy over my taking out Redwheels, and I am glad that neither he nor I could prevision the plight the shiny new runabout would be in before it was many hours older. With a stoical reserve he loaded in the two young lilacs that were in the exact state of sappiness Grandmother Nelson had recommended for transplanting, but his calmness nearly gave way when I had him put in a dandy old rake and spade and hoe that I had found in my raid on the cellar.

"Please ma'am, Miss Betty, don't go and leave ole mistis's gyarden tools out in no rain," he entreated, plaintively.

"Oh, Eph, are they really Grandmother Nelson's?" I exclaimed, with such radiance that it reflected from Eph's polished black face.

"Yes'm, and they is too good to be throwed away on playing gyarden or sich," he answered, with feeling.

"Eph," I answered, with almost a choke in my voice, "they'll be—be sacred to me. Oh, thank you for telling me."

"Go on, child! you shore is ole mistis herself, with your pretty words to push along your high-haided ways," he answered me while he gave Red-wheels an affectionate shove as I started down the street.

I didn't spend much time down-town, but I stopped at the post-office and got my mail to read while I waited at the drug-store for Mr. Simmons to put up some of every kind of flower and vegetable grandmother mentioned—if it was still in stock. He offered me a book of instructions, which I declined. I meant to garden by ancestral tendencies. And while I waited I looked over my letters. The volume from Peter I put aside to enjoy in a leisure hour, as I felt sure that I knew what was in it; but I opened another thin one that looked as if it might be from him, if he had written it in an unpoetic mood. It was from Judge Vandyne, and I then understood Peter's sudden determination to come down and live with Sam for a time, though I don't believe Peter knew the real reason of it himself. The judge is a great diplomat, and knows just when and to whom to be frank. We have always understood each other from the first vacation I spent with Mabel, and I value his confidence highly. He wrote:

No man can get a hold on the complex problems of this day and especially the next, who doesn't go at them with at least some sunburn on his neck and a few horny spots on his hands. Put Pete at it, you and Sam. Your description of Sam's habitation and vocation in letter to Mabel made me feel twenty-five again. I never had the real thing; but Peter shall. Ease him along. If he kicks over the traces let me know. When are you coming North again? Soon, I hope.

> Your aged admirer,
>
> PETER VANDYNE, Sr.

P. S.—Thought I'd better say that Dr. Herbrick doesn't like Peter's weight—one sixteen. You understand.

I wonder what the paternal Keats was like. I don't remember, and I must look him up to see. It's funny how sturdy-oak fathers can have ferny-mimosa sons. Mothers can stand producing poets, but it is hard on fathers. I felt that I must help out Judge Vandyne, and with that resolve I headed Redwheels out along Providence Road.

As I had told mother, the sobs and tears of the April day had been wilfully misleading demonstrations, for by ten o'clock the whole face of nature wore a sun-sweetened smile that was positively entrancing. The young April world seemed to spring dripping from a bath that glistened all over with crystal water gems. Winter is staid and dignified and grand with its stark trees and mantle of brown earth, and summer is glowing and glorious; but very young spring is so sappy and curly and yellow and green and lavender that you take it to heart and let it nestle there to suck its pink apple-blow thumb, and curl up its young sprout toes sheltered away from the cold that sets it back and the sun that forces it to break bud. Sometimes it stays with you a day and sometimes a week and a day, but you can't hold it back. You can just be thankful that you had it. I was.

But if the five miles of Providence Road had been
a delight, as Redwheels and I ran along it, the dirt
lane that led to The Briers was an intoxicating joy.
The wet earth, the drenched cedars, the oak buds,
the spongy moss, the reddening blackberry-bushes,
and the sprouting grain, all mingled in a queer
creation odor that went right through the pores of my
skin into my vitals and made me feel as strong as an
ox, or rather, as Sam's new mule. I caught a glimpse
of that mule through a vista before I came out of
the lane, plodding along before Sam and the plow
with a great splendid lurch of a gait that threw
the black dirt as high as Sam's knees as he plunged
along at the plow-handles. I stopped the car at the
cedar-pole gate of Eden and stood up and shouted
at the top of my lungs, but Sam plowed on hero-
ically, with never a glance in my direction, and I
just stood and looked at him and the mule. Seeing
a man plow cuts right down to the bottom of a
woman's nature, because I suppose it looks so—so
fundamental. At least that is about the way I felt
though it was much more so until I remembered
the blistered heel and shouted again, this time in
alarm. At my cry of distress Sam suddenly looked
up and jerked the mule's head so that he, too,
stopped and regarded me. They looked like wary
jungle things that had been belled from the thicket,
but for just a second; then Sam threw his line around
the plow-handle, thus hitching the mule to himself,
and came running across the field to me, as lightly
as the blue jay skimmed from over my head into

the branches of another cedar in answer to the same twit I had heard the day I first came out into the habitation of the birds. The pleasure of seeing Sam run to me was almost as keen as the pain of seeing him run away from me, but it was mitigated by my alarm over the poor sore foot.

"Gracious sakes, Betty! is that a mud-scow you came out in?" he asked, as he started to take my hand in his, which was brown with mud, and ended by rubbing his cheek in my palm. That seemed to be about the only member he had kept clean enough for the greeting.

"Aren't you hurting your heel plowing like that, Sam?" I asked, anxiously.

"Heel—what heel? Oh, that's all right. I haven't heard from it since you tucked it away in the cream Tuesday night. I have cold-bucketed myself every morning, standing on one leg with it up on the wash-bench so as not to wake it up. Come on up to the house. I'll walk, because I'm too muddy to get in with you in your sedan-chair."

"No; you go back to the plowing and I'll go and unload and begin my work," I answered, with positive heroism. I wanted to get out and go and be introduced to the mule, but I came to Sam to be not a clinging vine, but a competent garden-hoe to him.

"All right," said Sam, in the nice way he has of acquiescing in all my serious moods until they pass. "I'll be through after about three more rounds and then I'll come and help you. Say, Bettykin, what do you think of that for good land?" And as he looked back at the great square of black earth he had upturned, Sam's eyes flecked with the blue sky and snapped with enthusiasm.

"It looks good enough to eat," I answered, with a queer dirt enthusiasm rising in me that I had never even heard of one's having before.

"Yes, and you will eat it in about four months' time in the form of roasting ears," answered Sam, smacking his lips, which had a streak of the mud delicacy across them at right angles. "But go on up and tell Mammy to put your name in her dinner-pot and buy the Byrd to get you anything you need or want to the half of our kingdom. I'll be there in ten shakes of the mule's tail."

The road that leads from the cedar-pole gate through Sam's wilderness up to the farm-house curves in and out and around the hill past as many lovely spots as my enthusiasm could endure. Half-way up, there is a glimpse past a gray old tree with crimson thorns, of the valley with Old Harpeth looming opposite. Further on a rocky old road leads down around a clump of age-distorted cedar-trees to the moss-greened stone spring-house, from which the water gurgles and pours past Sam's huge earthern crocks of milk. Over it all broods the low white house on the plateau, from under whose wings I found one small blue chicken running and cheeping wildly for a ride up the hill.

The Byrd was, as usual, attired in miniatures of Sam's overalls, and his red mop stood on ends all over his head, while his freckles shone forth resplendently from the excitement of my arrival.

"Say, Betty, what you think? Old Buttercup found a calf out in the woods and it has got a white nose and two spots. Sam wanted to name it Chubb for the doctor that saved its life 'fore it got borned, but I said ladies first, and I calls it Betty. You can let it lick your fingers if Sam milks on 'em first. And Dominick have hatched 'fore the white hen—eleven, and one what Sam calls a half chicken, because he don't see how it is black when the eggs was bought thoroughbreds; but Mammy says because they is Yankee eggs. Come see all everything."

Sam's barn is an old tumble-down collection of sheds and the most lovely place I ever got into. It is running over with new-born life, and you can get an armful of first one variety and then another. I liked the collie puppies best, but the Byrd was crazy about the little fawn calf which old Buttercup is so proud of that she switches her tail in the greatest complacency. He was just showing me how to tempt her little white nose with a wisp of hay that she was learning to eat, and I was luxuriating with one new-born wriggler in my arms and two yellow-down puff-balls in my hand, when Sam and the mule came up from the field.

"My, it's great to have a nice family party like this to plow for!" he said, as he led the mule into his stall and poured down his oats out of a bucket the Byrd ran to bring him. "Any news from Petie, Bettykin?"

"I've got a letter from Peter that I haven't read,

THE BYRD WAS ATTIRED IN MINIATURES
OF SAM'S OVERALLS

but one from Judge Vandyne that I have. Here it is—read it," and I held the letter open for Sam to read over my shoulder.

"Read it to me, Betty; I'm too dirty to come that near you," he said, as he took the cob pipe out of his pocket and prepared to light up while the Byrd scampered to the house to hurry Mammy's dinner.

"You're not exactly dirty, Sam," I answered, surveying him with a satisfiedly critical eye. "You only look and smell like the earth and the sky and the barn and—and—"

"Just call it cosmic, Betty, and let it go at that," he answered, as he reached out and roughed my hair over my eyes with the long hickory switch with which he had been merely threatening the mule all day. "Go on, read me the judge's document on the subject of Peter while we wait for Mammy's dinner cluck."

As he had asked me to do, I read it all, slowly, while my heart, that had been climbing like a squirrel to the tops of the trees, began to burrow down in the reverse manner of a chipmunk. I could see Sam's spirits doing likewise.

"The judge gets under Pete's skin and peels the fat off him," said Sam, slowly, with sadness in his deep, strong voice. "I've just got to build some sort of a poet's corner to put him in, so he can come on down from Philadelphia from the opening of the spring Academy. He will have burned himself out by then, and he'll be so weak we can feed him out of a bottle."

6   69

"And it's his play, too, Sam," I answered, despondently. "He's beginning on the third act, and just reading it all and suggesting in spots is making me thin. It is all the terrible heroic struggle of the poor hero now and he doesn't seem to let the heroine help him a bit. Oh, Sam, if Peter were to fail with this play after Farrington has encouraged him I don't know what might happen! I'm sorry you ever mentioned Keats to me. I dream about him at night. I adored him when I was at The Manor, and so did Mabel," and my lips quivered so I had to turn against the harness hanging on the wall against which I drooped.

"Keats or Peter?" asked Sam as he pressed his whip across my shoulders in comforting little licks because his hand was too muddy to pat me.

"Both," I sniffed.

"Don't," said Sam, with cheering command in his voice. "We are too late to help Keats, and plenty early to pull Pete out of his divine fire. Let's go get some good grub from Mammy so we can plant the garden before sundown, and stake out the poet's corner, too. I didn't have the money to hire the plowing done, but I am almost through for the present; and I can whirl in now and get in shape for Petie's rescue in no time."

"It's popped its skin with stuffing, and Mammy says come on while the 'taters stands up stiff," announced the Byrd, half-way up the path from the house to the barn.

"He's talking about a duckling, but let's hope

70

Peter can be mentioned in the same terms in the near future," said Sam, as he drove the fleet Byrd and me before him with the switch, in a scamper to Mammy and food.

"Yes," said Sam, as he stood an hour later in the middle of the plot under the south window, which spread out in the sun like a great black lake, smooth from his repeated plowing and harrowing, "that is the richest bit of land at The Briers or in Benton County. It will bring some posies for you, Bettykin."

"I'm not going to plant just flowers in it, Sam," I answered in a tone that admitted of no discussion. "Do you remember the part of grandmother's book that told what she made off of the southern half-acre of hers the year everything failed? I've got it right here, and I'm going to follow it," and as I spoke I hugged the ancestral garden to my breast with one arm, while I held the old grass basket I had made for Sam in my infancy in the other hand, with all my town seeds in it.

"Oh, there's plenty of garden-land all over the place, Betty. Come on and sow the posies."

"There's not plenty of onion and beet and lettuce and okra and tomato and celery land right at the well, Sam, that Byrd and I can carry water from," I answered, positively. "Is this land mine or yours?"

"Yours."

"Wait. I forgot!" I exclaimed in sudden, embarrassed consternation. "Are you renting this land to me, Sam?"

"Renting it to you, Betty?" For a second Sam's eyes blazed in a way I hadn't seen since the time I didn't want to take all of the one fish we caught after a hot day's fishing out at Little Harpeth at our tenth and fourteenth years. Then, suddenly, a queer expression came up and drowned the anger in his eyes and twitched at the corners of his mouth until I recognized it as humor.

"I believe it would be better for us both to crop it on shares, as you are going to put in foodstuffs, too. I am cropping on onions with old Charlie Wade, down the road, and with sugar-beets with Hen Bates. In this case it would be about fair for you to furnish the seeds and I the land, all labor that each of us puts in to be charged against the gross receipts. I'll just enter you in my time-book now. Let's see—it is one-fifteen," and as he spoke Sam took out, first his watch, and then a muddy little book that had time-tables and all sorts of almanac things in it.

For a second I was as mad as I was when he handed me the two-inch fish and ordered me to take it in for the cook to have for my supper; but in a second I saw just what he had done to me and I didn't dare remonstrate.

"How much do I get an hour?" I asked, with the greatest dignity, as I threw the seed-basket and my hat on the ground and picked up my rusty old hoe, ready for business.

"I charge myself at twelve and a half cents. Are you worth about—about fifteen?" he asked in a business-like tone of voice, but I saw a twitch at the corners of his mouth that made me boil with rage.

"Put me down at six and a quarter for the present," I answered, haughtily.

"Down she goes," he answered, as he thus minimized me with his pencil and put the book back in his pocket. "Now, where do you want me to heave in the lilacs so as to get the two corners of the garden to guide the rows by? Shall they run north and south or east and west? It really doesn't make much difference."

"East and west, then," I answered, calmly, though my hand clenched over the hollyhock seeds which I had put in an envelope in the pocket of my corduroy skirt. It was cruelly thoughtless of him —this selection of the lilacs for the corner-stones of the garden after making me so happy, not a month ago, with that lovely sentiment about wanting to plant the hollyhock seeds first in memory of the dolls of our youth. "Peter will enjoy looking down the rows from the living-room window better than across them," I added, quickly, for fear he would humiliate me by remembering that he had forgotten the hollyhock seeds he had stolen for me.

"Say where and I'll dig for you," he said; but I saw a glint of something fairly shoot from his eyes.

"Here," I said, and stood at a nice right angle from the corner of the house and the old cedar-tree he had said he could nail the wires to to save a post, when he had to put up a fence.

He came over promptly with the spade and poised it to dig into the ground—and my heart.

Then he hesitated, and looked at me quickly for a second. Then he threw down the spade and said, quietly:

"I'll go get that rotted stump dirt before I break ground for the lilacs, and you can think about things while you wait." With that he lifted the wheelbarrow and trundled out of the situation, leaving me in the depths of a hurt uncertainty.

But if Samuel Foster Crittenden thought I was as stupid as that, he had a chance to learn better— at least I thought I would give him one. I'm not sure yet that I did.

As soon as he was out of sight I flew to the end of the garden, where I thought the row of hollyhocks would make a lovely background for all the long lines of vegetables and flowers running into it, sighted with my eye, ran a trench with the rusty old hoe, flung in my seeds, and covered it up in less time than it takes to tell it. When Sam came back I had spaded out at least two and a half shovelfuls of dirt, that I found surprisingly heavy, from the hole for the first lilac. I saw him start and hesitate as if about to say something, and then I think —I think, but I can't be sure—his eyes rested on my hasty and surreptitious gardening.

"You are the real thing, Betty," was all he said as he roughed my hair, first back and then down over my eyes, and took Grandmother Nelson's spade from my hand and began to make the dirt fly out of the hole. I wonder what I'll say when those hollyhocks come up.

And then we all worked. It astonished me to find what one man, one woman, and one small boy can do to a plot of earth in three hours, with a string, sharpened sticks, seed, hoes, spades, rakes, and radiant happiness. At four o'clock we all three sank down in a heap at the end of the last row of green peas in delicious exhaustion.

"Nice little seed, I'll dig you up to-morrow to see how you feel," said the Byrd as he patted in a stray pea he had found with the beets. "I can't dig you all up, but I will as many as I can."

"Yes, you will—not," said Sam, reaching for him as he skimmed and dipped away. And then followed a lecture on floriculture, agriculture, and horticulture that I immensely enjoyed.

"Yes," assented the fledgling, with the greatest intellectual enthusiasm, "baby beets folds up jest that way," and he illustrated after Sam, with his grubby little paddies, "same as chickens in eggs and—"

"Come on, Betty, let's go select the spot for the cedar-log temple for Peter's muses," Sam interrupted as he made a lightning grab for the Byrd and tumbled him back into the loamy earth.

I realized then that up to a quarter of five o'clock on that twenty-first-of-April day I had been really wretchedly uneasy about Peter in every way, that I did and did not understand since that scene at the tea-table in the Astor when I had assumed the re-

sponsibility of him. But at that moment when Sam
held back a tangle of blackberry-bushes and low-
sweeping dogwood boughs, and we stepped out on a
moss-covered rock-ledge that commanded a view
of the Harpeth Valley, stretching away and away in
an iridescent shimmer of springiness and sunshine,
it completely vanished, for the time being, anyway.

"Oh," I said, with a great sigh of relief, "let's
plant Peter here. He—he can grow his dream in
this place."

"Yes," answered Sam, quietly, "I'll log up and
daub up a shack right here, with a stone fireplace.
It won't cost anything, for I'll use my own logs and
pick up my own stones. Thank God for shoulders
and arms which can make shelter for anybody that
needs it anywhere," and as he spoke Sam looked
across the valley into the blaze of the sun that was
beginning to go down behind Paradise Ridge, with
that earth-smolder I was beginning to recognize.
I knew that David and Moses and Christ had all
looked down across new life from a hillside, and Sam
seemed almost transfigured to me. And I had a—
a vision. I saw that Sam was to be one of a gigantic
new kind of men to whom all who were ahungered
and athirst would come to be cared for. I had
brought Peter to him first, and I knew—I felt that
others—that—

"Sam," I said, as I reached out and laid a timid
hand, for the first time stained with earth labor,
on the blue sleeve of his overalls, "don't ever leave
Peter and me anywhere you are not, will you?"

"I'm always here for you both when you need me, Betty. Just call," he answered. "And now you hustle home to Mother Hayes or she won't let me have you at six and a quarter cents any more."

"Make it five, Sam. I feel smaller now."

"No, that 'll be Pete's rate. Come on and take the mud-scow back to Eph. Present my compliments to him after he has washed it."

Some people have a way of pruning a friend's spirit in a manner that makes it bush out more hardily than ever. That is the way Sam does me, and I intend to worship him delightfully if I want to and he continues to deserve it. It is so much better for a woman to worship a man than love him; it puts a strong barrier between them to keep him from hurting her, which loving him doesn't seem to, at least not with Edith and Tolly; and I am always worried over Peter; but for long intervals I can forget Sam comfortably and find him right there when I need him.

I am glad that I had that care-free day of hard work with Sam out at The Briers to fatigue me so that I couldn't take Peter's letter completely to heart. I read it, cried over it a minute, and then fell into my bed without even putting rose oil on my cheek curls to hold them in place. My first day at farming had done me up. Still, it's no use to cover up your head from trouble; it's right here by the bed the minute you peep over the top of the sheet. I woke up, feeling that the whole world must be camping on the top of my crocheted lace counterpane; but soon I realized that it was only Peter's play. Peter is stuck in the mud at the beginning of the third act, and he thinks it is quicksands that are going to drown him. The last few sentences of the letter sound like a beautiful funeral oration to himself, and they made me so miserable that I put on my clothes and fled to daddy, who was out smoking his cigar on the front porch in the crisp morning air.

"And Sam can't possibly get ready for him to come down in less than two weeks. He has to build the house in between the plowing and milking and other things. Peter may die. What shall we do?" I wound up with a wail.

"Sam paid off the note on two of the cows and cash for the mule last Monday," answered daddy. "Not a farmer in the Harpeth Valley has done better in less than two years, and I would leave Peter to him. I guess he can fodder up the play, too. Have the poet down to visit mother while he waits."

"He can't come for a week; he's going to be decorated at the Academy. He's the youngest that ever has been; but I'll write and ask him," I answered, in a jumble, but very much comforted.

Peter accepted my invitation and announced his arrival as ten days later. Then real work began among Sam's friends and mine in Hayesboro.

I put the case to them plainly and movingly. Here was a young and distinguished genius coming to settle down in Hayesboro to rescue his play,

78

and it was the duty of everybody to help him in every way. The first thing he had to have was shelter, and we ought to all help Sam as much as we could to provide it for him. He was willing to stay with us for a few days, on mother's invitation, which I had to hide nine crochet-needles to make her write him, but he wrote that his "spirit panted for the wilderness," and if he felt that way about it he ought to be settled in the cabin as soon as possible.

"Why, of course," said Julia, with large and responsive enthusiasm," we must just all turn in and help Sam. I never helped build a house, but if you can, Betty, so can I."

"I can make curtains and things and cushions for chairs," said Edith, with no less enthusiasm than Julia's. "I have a lovely bureau-scarf all finished and—"

"Chairs — bureau!" I fairly gasped. "Neither Sam nor I had thought of furniture. Sam paid a big note in the bank for the cows and mule, and how can he buy more stock like chairs and bureaus and beds?"

"Why, hasn't Sam got furniture? The Crittenden house had the loveliest in Hayesboro," asked Edith, plaintively.

"He's sold it; Sam is poor," I answered, proudly. "He hasn't got anything but Mammy and Byrd and the other stock, and places for all to sleep and eat and keep warm. Now what are we going to do?"

"He wouldn't let us buy him anything, would he?" asked Sue, thoughtfully.

"I know Sam better than that," said Edith.

"I'll tell you," I exclaimed, suddenly and radiantly. "Of course, we can't give Sam anything, but I believe—I believe that if I asked him very kindly he would let us make a kind of museum of affection of Peter's room and take all the lovely things we can borrow from people to put in the shack to help inspire him. Mother will let me start with Grandmother Nelson's desk, though it is dearer than life to me; and I know she'll crochet him a lamp-mat before he gets here—maybe several, if she likes the pattern she starts on."

"Do you remember that mahogany table in my room?" exclaimed Julia, several minutes lost in deep reflection. "It is real Chippendale, Aunt Amanda says, and I'll send that out. Oh, to think of a poet laying his pen down on it! Or does he use a pencil?"

And it is true that from very small beginnings great trees grow. In this case it was Peter's roof-tree, or rather what was under it. I never saw anything like Hayesboro when it takes generosity in its teeth and runs away, as at the time when Mr. Stanton, the Methodist minister, had thirty-five pounds of sausage sent him from different hog-killings just because in prayer-meeting, when he publicly thanked the Lord for his seventh child, he mentioned that it was welcome, though one more mouth to feed. Of course, the baby didn't need the sausage any more than Peter really needed all the things everybody wanted to send out to make

the cabin comfortable for him. Fortunately, Sam
kept his head, as the minister did when he sold the
sausage and bought groceries for the whole family;
he selected only five pieces out of the list of sixty
that we gave him, and it took me a day and a half
to go around and keep people from getting hurt
because he didn't call in his wagon for the things
they had got out and rubbed and dusted. And before the sun set on the second day of my explanations
I had talked Peter into the very heart of Hayesboro,
which was all down to the station to meet him and
welcome him. The mayor wanted to have the
brass band, but I persuaded him not to do that,
but to make Peter a little speech. Miss Henrietta
Spain asked to have her school children march down
to throw jonquils in his path, and I had to give in
to that. Besides, I thought Peter would like it;
so did Sam.

But that came later, after six of the longest days
any of us ever lived through. We spent them at
The Briers, and every soft friend I had is now a
hardened specimen. Everybody went out to see
Sam and advise him about how to care for a distinguished guest that they all felt that Hayesboro
owned and was just lending to Sam for the time
being, and they all remained to farm. Most of
them had never been to see him before, and they
were so delighted that they lost their heads and hearts
to the farm. The Briers is like a great, big, beautiful
dog that lies there begging you to come and plow
it and scratch it and hoe it and rake it, while it

licks out green curly vegetable tongues for more.
At first Sam seemed slightly overwhelmed by all
the offers of help that came with me in Redwheels,
dressed in business-like corduroys that had been
made like mine, in a hurry, and with hoes and seed-
baskets, or that Pink or Tolly drove out in their
cars; but he finally entered everybody in the time-
book at two and a half cents an hour, gave each a
plot of ground that wouldn't do for anything else,
and started them off, while he kept on at real work.
I'm glad to have every healthy assurance of being
in the world when Sam comes to the harvesting of
his friendly crops. It will be a great occasion.
If Edith's five rows of okra do not net or gross—
I forget which is the right term for it—I know she
will wilt away, and I dread Sue if her fifty tomato-
plants go down before the humble cutworm. Sue
won't be humble. Miss Editha came out with
us one afternoon and sowed a row of ladies'-slippers
and princess-feathers, and it was funny to see old
Dr. Chubb, who had driven the ten miles just for
the pleasure of seeing Sam (only, Sam said it was in
hopes of seeing me), digging and raking for her,
while Colonel Menefee, in true military style, commanded them both. Father came once and took
Sam away down to a field by himself, and from the
look on both their faces I was afraid Sam had again
refused to borrow money to buy the mate to the
mule he needed so badly. Father was so mad he
took off his coat, and he and Tolly split wood enough
for the big fireplace to last until midsummer. Sam

says that Pink sweat enough soap-grease to make him worth more than two and a half cents, if it could have been collected. He didn't mean us to hear him say it to Pink, but Edith got pale with shock, while daddy roared so that old Buttercup came up the hill to see what was the matter. Julia laughed, and so did I—when we got away from Edith.

It took six good days of such chorus work to get every odd job at The Briers nicely finished up, and daddy and the mayor and Colonel Menefee mended all the rail fences before they rested on the seventh.

Then on Monday morning came the log-raising for the poet's lodge, and everybody assembled long before Sam had nicked the last log with his great big adz. We all sat around on the rocks and ends of the logs and discussed how to begin before Sam got ready to tell us the right way. The colonel and Miss Editha were standing a little to one side, and I knew that he was being sentimental by the fluttering smile that came and went on her tea-rose face; but suddenly he turned and said to daddy, with his fierce old face lighting:

"Just look, Hayes, there's pioneer blood in them yet—and brawn, too," he added, as Tolly and Pink and Billy Robertson stripped off their coats and came forward as Sam knocked the last crimson cedar chip from the last log.

"Steady—up now, Tolly," said Sam, as Tolly bent to one end of one of the long, rough cedar logs, that had so lately been a forest king, but that was now dethroned and shorn of its branching power with which to wrestle with the wind. Pink and Billy got holds in between. "Up—up, boys! Now roll!" shouted Sam again, and with a strain and a heave they landed the first log level and true on the stone underpinnings.

"Hip—hip—hurrah for the poet's house!" shouted Tolly, as he rolled his shirt-sleeves up and spat on his hands to show his readiness for more logs; and we all clapped, while Edith picked up a button that had popped off his shirt with the strain of his big chest underneath.

Then for a second Sam's kind eyes sank down deep into mine and smoldered there. I know he was praying for Peter as the rest cheered. Then he bent and called out:

"Next. Up—up, boys! Steady!"

My eyes misted for a second, and Peter's pale face rose before them in the mist. Peter is a man of dreams, for whom was being harnessed all this sinew and brawn of reality. And men must plow and plant and reap and hew and lift for their vision-bringers, and women must do it also. It is only right. I am willing. Where were the neighbors to the Keatses that they didn't— And I was about to be dissolved in a sea of sentiment when Sam's voice hauled me to the surface as he shouted:

"Hi, Betty, get out and sight this end for a right angle-drop, as I showed you. Wait! Back, boys!"

And after that I held the metal square and

sighted until I felt as if I had eaten a right angle, while Sam's crew heaved and raised and dropped and rolled, until all four of the low walls were fitted into the notches, log for log, and the roof-poles were laid just as the sun began to quit his job and get on toward China.

"No four of their young Virginia pioneer ancestors who came over the wilderness trail did it any quicker or better, Colonel," said daddy, as he walked around to the back of the cabin and then again to the front. As he spoke he laid his arm across Sam's shoulder—and I knew that the breach was healed until the next time daddy tried to help him financially.

All the log-raisers went home by twilight, and daddy and I were the last. The Byrd had insisted on showing daddy nine little curly-tailed pigs taking their evening repast at the maternal fount, which they were shyly late in doing because the fledgling perched so near them on the fence to exhibit and direct the repast.

This left me to help Sam gather up his tools and pick up the fragrant cedar chips for Mammy's vesper fire.

"Now, the chimney next and Pete's housed," said Sam, as he sat down on a log right where I was crouching, filling the basket with the chips. "Are you happy, Bettykin?"

"Sam, when I know that Peter is tucked in that little old bed that matches yours that mother gave you out of our garret I am going to breathe so deep that maybe I'll—I'll break my belt," I answered, as I picked a chip from under one of his big farm shoes. "I couldn't stand him on my mind much longer."

"Let him stay comfortably in your heart and don't get him on your mind," answered Sam, as he calmly got out the cob pipe, filled and lighted it. "Pete's great enough to fill both for any woman." And Sam's face took on that devout young prophet-look it always does when he looks at his land or mentions Peter—the look which then began to irritate as well as impress me, I don't exactly know why.

"My mind's not very big and my heart is smaller," I snapped, as I upset part of the basket of chips and had to begin to pick them all up again.

"You're young—you'll grow up—to Pete," said Sam, as he roughed my hair worse than he had ever done since I had forbidden him, picked up my basket and started to the house, leaving me to follow, squaw-fashion and perfectly furious. Now if I don't know whether my troth is plighted to Peter, and Peter doesn't know, I am certain that I can't see why Samuel Foster Crittenden should be so sure of it; and he and I parted anything but friends, a fact over which I could feel daddy chuckle as he sat wedged beside me in the car, though he didn't dare smile. I would wager my first mess of peas that he winked at Sam. I had seen them act that way about me only too often in my infancy. I felt that I hated the whole world until I had to except the fledgling, who rode down to the gate on the running-board just over my left shoulder, while Sam came along to hold him on.

"Betty, you is the prettiest lady they is if your eyes do crinkle when you laugh, and ain't blue. I'd let you kiss me anywhere I'm clean enough, if you bring me just one pigeon that will lay eggs for little ones," he said, as I slowed up for him to climb down to open the gate.

"She could get one cheaper than that, Byrd," said Sam, as he got down to open the gate, while for a second I snuggled the fledgling, whom I always hated to leave out in the woods in the dark, even with Sam's rough hand so near his pillow.

"Thank you," I said, pleasantly, as I drove through the gate, without stopping another ten minutes to chat, as I knew daddy wanted to. I'm glad Samuel Foster Crittenden will never know just exactly what I was cross about, as I wasn't sure myself. It is strange how you can hate a person for whom you have the deep regard I have for Sam, when he has done nothing at all to offend you.

That night I fought it all out with myself about Peter. I felt that Sam had brought the sore spot in my heart to head and I would have to operate and find out what was really there. Accordingly, after I had safely anchored myself in the middle of my old four-poster bed I slashed myself. This is what I found. That I had made up my mind to marry Peter just as soon as he wanted me to, which I knew would not be until after the play was finished down in Sam's wilderness. I had two reasons for my intention. Nobody in the world ever loved and depended on me as Peter has always done since he read me the winning poem that he sent in for his Junior Prize. Peter needs me, and nobody else in the world does. What could love be but giving and cherishing the beloved? By the test of how I longed to do all that to Peter I found out how I loved him. That was the reason I openly admitted, but I am afraid that I was afraid of Sam if I should fail his young David-Keats in any way. He had already warned me what I must be to him, and I felt as I did about that heifer I let get by me the first day I went to dig Sam out of the hollow tree to which he has now had to build a new crotch in order to take in Peter. This time I would head off his calf for him, though I didn't mean to call Peter that, even in the heat of debate with myself. Oh, I could take such good care of Peter and Judge Vandyne, and Mabel would be so glad! My spirits rose at the thought of their joy, and as I felt better, I luxuriated in the thought of Sam's approbation. I would give Peter the answer he had begged for in every letter, help him with the play until it was finished, and then have a glorious wedding, with Edith and Sue and Julia and all the girls. I must have fallen asleep then, for I dreamed that Julia was the bride at my wedding and that I couldn't get there. When I woke from that nightmare I decided to let Sam have the happiness of hearing Peter tell him of my submission to their wishes; and that time I sobbed myself to sleep.

THE BOOK OF SHELTER

From that fatal night until the afternoon of Peter's arrival, I saw Sam only three times, and those when there were many others with us. I was so sweet and submissive to him that I saw I alarmed him greatly.

Peter arrived according to schedule and was met in the manner planned by our friends. As he stood on the train platform just behind a woman and a baby, I saw his great dark eyes, that seem fairly to glow out of his beautiful face, eagerly race over the crowd. When they rested on me they lit with what I thought was perfect joy until I saw them find Sam a few seconds later. That was the real thing, and I never loved Peter better than when I saw him hold Sam's hand in his while he was greeting me in a suppressed, lover-like way and was being introduced to people. Sam was also radiant. Peter and Sam and I are the eternal triangle that Peter is always talking into plots for plays—only Sam is the apex instead of me. Isn't it beautiful to have it that way?

III

THE BOOK OF LAUGHTER

HAYESBORO took Peter into its heart of hearts and then sighed for more to give him. This town is like the old man's horse whose natural gait is running away when it is not asleep. Peter woke it up and it took the bit in its mouth and bolted with him, while Peter clung to the saddle and had the time of his young poetic life.

Mother accepted Peter with her usual placidity. She took him into her room and I suppose she examined him physically, for I saw her give him a dose of sarsaparilla tea every morning he was with us. I bought her five spools of the finest silk thread, ranging in shade from gray to lavender, to begin on a crocheted tie and pair of socks for him. Daddy was as good as gold to him and fell immediately into Judge Vandyne's attitude toward him. I knew he would. Eph maintained the dignity of the haphazard family at meal-times, and waited on Peter worshipfully at all others. The black beauty in the kitchen was heard to remark to the house-girl:

"I hope that white man's skin will stretch, for I shore am going to stuff it. He am a insult to any respectable skillet or pot." She did, and at times I trembled for the poet.

He read to Miss Henrietta Spain's school the poem on "Space" which the *Literary Opinion* had copied; and he was the greatest possible success. Most of it I feel sure the school didn't understand. But just as he finished the last two lines—those lines the magazine had called "as perfect in winged lyric quality as any lines in the English language could be"—the Byrd, whom Sam had groomed carefully and brought in from the brier-patch for the occasion, rose, and, with his freckles black with the intensity of his comprehension of the poem, spread his little arms and said:

"I fly! I fly!"

"I fly! I fly, too!" A little chubkin in a blue muslin dress just behind him jumped to her feet and echoed him before they could be repressed.

"That was the most perfect tribute I shall ever receive," Peter said, that night out on the porch, after Sam had gone home, carrying the exhausted Byrd, who even in sleep held in one hand the handle of a full basket he had begged from mother, and in the other tightly grasped a sack in which were two "little ones" daddy had got for him. These treasures happened to be young rabbits, and Sam said he would charge daddy with the damages.

"Good old Sam," said Peter, as we stood at the gate by the old lilac, who was beginning to beplume himself more richly than any of his compatriots in Hayesboro—in honor of Peter, I felt sure—and watched Sam and the Byrd jog away in the wagon down Providence Road. "He'll make his mark on his generation yet, Betty. This is just a temporary eclipse of the effulgence of a young planet that will shine with the warm light of humanity when the time comes. There is no man like him. O Samboy!"

"Oh, I love you, Peter, for feeling that way," I exclaimed, heartily, as I grasped his arm with enthusiasm. "You are so wonderful, Peter."

"Dear, dearest Betty," said Peter, as he put his arm through mine, and we both began to swing back and forth on the gate. "It is so marvelous to have a woman respond to your every mood as you do to mine. It is like having in one's possession an angel incarnate in her own harp."

"Oh, Peter you *are* wonderful!" I again exclaimed, because I felt that way and had no other feeling to draw another remark from. It is so satisfactory to love a man with no variations. I cannot see why girls like to tremble and blush and chill and glow and get angry and repentant about the men they love, as Edith does about Clyde Tolbot. I wish I could make them all understand the great calmness of true love like mine for Peter.

The five days that Peter stayed with mother, Hayesboro did many other things to him. The mayor got up a barbecue in his honor, and they had nine political speeches and two roast pigs and a lamb. Peter came home pale, but we decided before we went to bed to let the hero of "The Emergence " get beaten up a little in the strike before he made his great speech to the capitalist. I felt so happy for the play.

But the next day Peter took tea alone with Miss Editha Morris Carruthers, and he was so charmed with her that he almost decided to let the whole play end in separation.

"But it is so lonely for a woman to be a heroine of a separation, Peter," I pleaded with him as we sauntered up and down the long porch.

"Under such stress souls grow, Betty," he answered, glcomily. "Together lovers feed on the material; apart, on the immaterial. Can we say which is best for the final emergence of the superman and—" Just here Julia came across the street and into our front gate, looking like a ripe peach, in a pink muslin gown, with a huge plate of hickory-nut butter-candy in her hand, and we all three proceeded to material nourishment. I left them for a few minutes while I went up to my room and took out Grandmother Nelson's book. I wanted to be sure that not a single thing would bloom before I got back to The Briers. Peter had insisted that he should not go forth into the wilderness until he could do it dramatically to stay, so I hadn't been out for five days or more and I was wild—simply mad. To have a garden and be separated from it at sprouting and blooming time is worse than any soul separation that ever happened to any woman. Of that I feel sure.

Sue Bankhead was as nice and lovely to Peter

as could be, and even Billy Robertson's contentment with himself was slightly ruffled with the way she took him out horseback with her every morning, but her crowning attention was a dance for him. Sue has the loveliest dances in Hayesboro because of her own charm and the fact that the double parlors in the old Bankhead house are sixty-two feet long and forty-six feet wide. The girls were as lovely as a bunch of spring blossoms, and Julia looked like the most gorgeous, pink, fragrant, drooping cabbage-rose as Peter danced with her again and again. I was so glad, because he is as tall as she is, and she is such a good dancer that it must have been as soothing to his tired nerves as a nice wide rocking-chair with billows of blue mull cushions. It was easy to see what she thought of him from the way she looked at him, and poor Pink took me out in the moonlight and swore at me in polite language.

"Why don't you feed your sick poet your own self, Betty, and not let him loose to eat up my girl?" he stormed.

"Oh, Pink, how can you be so ungenerous, when you know how wonderful he is and how wonderful his play will be if you and everybody are kind and good to him while he is writing it," I chided him.

"Well, he had better not put Julia into it without me," he answered, somewhat mollified at my reproof.

"He won't, I know he won't," I hastened to assure him. "Especially if you are nice to him, as you promised. You know, Pink, you are an awfully interesting man in some ways, and I know it is going to do Peter a lot of good to be friends with you; you are so—so substantial."

"That's it; slap my fat! Everybody does," he answered, gloomily.

"It was the mules I was talking about, not you, Pink," I answered, hurriedly, for I know how sensitive he is.

"Well, call me a mule then," he again said, with the deepest depression.

"Now don't be stupid, Pink, and—"

"I am stupid, too!"

"Pink Herriford, will you please tell my friend, Peter Vandyne, about your heroism in stopping the stampede of those thousand mules you were shipping to France in time to save the lives of all of them and about ten men? I seem to have to speak to you in words of two syllables to-night." I could feel my cheeks burn with temper as I spoke and Pink came immediately out of his grouch and into his own happy personality.

"Holy smoke! Betty, but that was some stunt! First I saw a big red mule lift his hind legs in ugly temper, and let fly right and left just as—"

"Oh, wait Pink, let me get Peter!" I exclaimed, as I heard the dance that Pink and I had been arguing out, instead of sitting or dancing out, stop to get breath.

Pink was a wonder as he stood in the center of everybody that I had gathered around him to hear in particular what they had all been talking about in general. We were all spellbound, for it was a really exciting and tremendous recital, and even Julia came out of her daze over Peter to listen with rapt attention, though I imagine she had heard it before.

"Immense!" exclaimed Peter, with his pale, thin face in a perfect flame of excitement just as Pink threw his own body right in front of the largest mule and turned his neck and—

"What?" said Pink, as he glared at Peter suspiciously.

"Perfectly great," said Peter, laying his arm on Pink's. "And I don't see—"

Just here I slipped out onto the porch and sat down on the steps in the starlight to get my breath while the tale of heroism went on from the reassured hero.

. And as I stood on the front steps, just out of the noise of "Too Much Mustard" that had again begun its syncopated wail in the house, I began to worry about all my flower children in the country. Sam had not been in for three days, and he had sent word by one of his neighbors that he couldn't get to the dance because he had to cup up potatoes to plant. He had explained to Byrd and me all about how you cut out each little eye with some potato around it for moisture and nourishment while it takes root in the earth, and the Byrd had been especially interested in all the potato-peels ever since. He had almost worn the life out of Mammy begging her not to cut through any of the "little ones" with her knife until she had taken to boiling them whole. And as I sat and pictured them all sitting on the back porch with the big lamp lighted, just cutting away, maybe Byrd still up for the emergency, the whole dance seemed to put on a mask of grinning foolishness and resolve itself, with its jiggy music, into a large bunch of nothing, with me included. I was in a bad way for the best dancer in Hayesboro, not to sound like boastful Billy.

"Well, hello! Can this be Betty the wall-flower?" called a voice from over the fence. It was so out of sight that it might have come from the hollow log out on Old Harpeth if it hadn't been so near. "Won't anybody dance with you, honey-bunch?"

"Nobody; unless you will," I answered, running down toward the voice. And as I came nearer the hedge I saw that a wagon and mule were drawn up in the shadow behind a man. "It's fine for you to come in, after all, Sam. Peter will be so happy."

"Overalls are not invited," answered Sam, as he gave my hair the usual rough with his big horny hand while I reached up and grasped his sleeve, too glad to see him to remonstrate. "I came in for Pete's things, and I brought a load of new peas and ten dozen eggs at the same time, so I couldn't dress for the dance, or have time to dance if I did. Six seventy-five a barrel, and five barrels; how's that for wealth, Bettykin?" As he spoke Sam reached down in his overalls pocket, brought up a big fistful of all kinds of money, and poured it into my tunic of embroidered mull that I held up for it.

97

"It is the most beautiful money I ever saw," I said, and I had to swallow hard to keep out of my voice the sentiment I knew Sam would not like. I knew how hard he had worked for every cent of it.

"I'll give you that bright new quarter if you think it is so pretty," he said, and of course it couldn't have been emotion that cut his voice off so indistinctly.

"Come on, then, and let me dance for it," I answered. Then myself and money and mull dress,—that came all the way from New York with a three-figured bill—I threw into the blue-jeans arms. And out on the smooth, hard turnpike Sam and I had one glorious fox-trot with only the surprised mule looking on.

"Bring Pete out at about eleven. Your first pea is due to pod about noon. No, I must go now or never," said Sam as he shook me off when I clung and begged for another dance. He climbed up in the wagon. "Good night," he called.

For a long time I stood and watched him standing bolt upright in the wagon and clattering away with his great ugly old mule in a lurching trot; then I went in to the dance. I didn't tell anybody that Sam had been there, because they would all have been disappointed. The way Sam's home town loves him and disapproves of his farming is pathetic. Five miles is a long way for anybody that knows Sam to be separated from him, at least that is the way I felt as Peter slid and skidded and dipped me around while he told me how proud he was of my beauty and the lovely and worthy friends I possessed. He mentioned Julia and Pink and the mules in detail. I think Peter Vandyne has the most grateful, appreciative, sympathetic nature I ever encountered, and I told him so as we walked home across the lawn while the stars were beginning to grow pale and flicker with no more night to burn.

"My heart is full, full, dear, dearest Betty, with you and—and the work. The vision becomes clearer," Peter said, with his great dark eyes looking up at the retreating stars. And as we walked up the steps he told me another struggle he had thought up for the hero to have with his conscience about the poor little waiting heroine. The mule story hadn't done him one bit of good, and I went to bed as cross as two sticks.

"Oh, Samboy! I'm glad you are there and that you are Peter's next of friends or first or— Good night!" I muttered, as I closed my eyes on my favorite glimpse of Old Harpeth.

The next morning at about nine-thirty occurred Peter Vandyne's introduction into real life. He took it gallantly with his head up and swimming for shore.

The day was one of young May's maiden efforts offered with a soft smile of tender sunshine and in a flutter of bird wing and apple-blow. Of course, Sam had told me not to bring Peter out to The Briers until about eleven o'clock, because he wanted to do some farm housekeeping, as I afterward found out. But half past nine was the very limit of my endurance, and I sat and fidgeted with the wheel while mother and Eph packed us up with the inevitable basket for Byrd plus the also inevitable "little ones" that daddy somehow managed to find for him. These young were three small kittens, attended in their blindness by a black-and-white-spotted mother cat, all safely laced into a large basket and by that time resigned to their fate. I didn't mean to be disrespectful to dear Peter in my thoughts, but somehow they reminded me of him as he was led to farm life; and I laughed outright as Eph gave Peter a parting pat and Redwheels and me a shove, while mother called after us not to forget the sarsaparilla.

As long as I live I shall remember that journey along old Providence Road with a lovely nature like Peter's. He glowed with his inward flame there at my side, until I felt that it would be bad for him. Peter has seen all kinds of wonderful scenery all his life; but of course, there is none in the world anything like the Harpeth Valley. All the other in the world is either grand or placid or swept and garnished and tended or brilliant or moist, but this valley under Paradise Ridge is different. Peter expressed it so that my throat tightened and I had to hold steadier to the wheel as we passed an old farm wagon.

"It's the hollow of God's hand in which He has gathered His children and their homes, Betty," he said, huskily. "Look at that white-haired old grand dame in her frilled frock with the string of chickens following her and the two kiddies bringing up the rear. And look at that old red-gray brick house. England has nothing finer."

"That is old Mrs. Georgetta Johnson," I answered, as I waved my hand and got a stately wave in return. "She is the fifth generation to live in that house, and the two kiddies are the eighth. Her mother danced with Lafayette, and she is over eighty-five. I'll take you to see her some day."

"Betty," said Peter, with positive awe, "I have never seen such homes and furniture and people as I have found here. What is it that makes it so—so satisfying?"

"It must be that everything has had time to root here, people and all," I answered as I again avoided a farm wagon and a negro driving two fine milk-cows with cow babies wobbling along at their flanks.

"Yes," answered Peter, thoughtfully—"yes, I should say that 'rooted' would about express the life, and I am wondering—" But just here we turned off into Brier Lane, and Peter went up in the air and began to float among the tree-tops, only being able to take in the high-lights like the gnarled old cedars that jutted out from the lichen-covered stone wall and hung over the moss-green snake-rail fences, or the old oaks which were beginning to draw young, green loveliness around them, or the feathery buck-bushes and young hackberries that were harboring all varieties of mating birds who were wooing and flirting and cheeping baby talk in a delightfully confidential and unabashed manner. Peter had become wildly absorbed in a brilliant scarlet cardinal that

8

followed the car, scolding and swearing in the most
pronounced bird language, all for no fault of ours
that we could see, when we turned in the cedar-
pole gate of The Briers and began to wind our way
up through the potato and corn field on one side
and the primeval forest on the other. It was difficult to get Peter past the old thorn-tree view of the
Harpeth Valley we had come through, and he
wanted to get out and stay for ever at the milk-house;
but I finally landed him in a Homeric daze up in
front of the house, which stood with its hospitable
old door wide open but deserted.

"Sam! Byrd! Mammy!" I shouted at the top
of my lungs, while Peter sat paralyzed at the sight
of Sam's farm-house. Peter had got the old Crittenden house and all the others where he had been
entertained in his mind's eye, and that Sam's present
residence was a shock to him I could see plainly.
That was the beginning.

"Hi, Betty, come here quick—I need you!" came
in Sam's most business-like voice from the barn up
on the hill, while I could hear wild and excited cheeps
from the Byrd and disturbed clucks from Mammy.

Leaving Peter to disembark as he recovered himself, I sped around the house and up to the barn.

"Here, Betty, this blamed mule has kicked old
Jude, and I must have somebody to hold the edges
together while I sew it up. Mammy's hands aren't
steady enough. Now press the edges together and
never mind the blood on your hands. Hold the
halter, Mammy. You get that can of lime ready to

dust it, Byrd." Thus in dirty, blood-stained overalls, with his hair on ends and an earth smudge as usual right across his face like a Heidelberg scar, Sam was commanding his forces of nature.

"Ugh—uu—ow, Sam," I shivered; but I came up under his arm and tried to push one dripping section of old-roan hide until it joined the other, though I couldn't quite make it. Over my shoulder Sam began to sew it across with a huge crooked needle, helping me push the edges together as best he could. At this auspicious moment the poet appeared at the barn door in an absolutely dazed condition.

"Here you, Pete, too!" Sam commanded, without looking up. "Get here on the other side and press the hide together as Betty is doing. This is an awful long cut, but I can manage it, thanks to seeing Chubb sew up Bates's mule. Whoah, Jude, old girl! Hold her steady, Mammy! Now, Pete, press hard; never mind the blood!"

At Sam's determined reiteration of the word blood, my senses reeled, and if it had been anybody but Sam sewing over my shoulder, I would have gone down in a crumpled heap. Also I was stirred by one glance at Peter's lovely long oval face with its Keats lock of jet-black hair tossed aloft, and I remained conscious from astonishment.

This was a new Peter. His eyes burned in his face with determination. He squared his legs, clad in his elegant idea of farming corduroys, at the exact angle at which Sam's were set; then his long, white hands pulled the bloody old hide together exactly in place.

"That's it, Pete, hold it there. You slip out, Betty, and hold Jude while Mammy gets the hot water ready to wash it when it is finished. Now, Pete, an inch farther along! Whoah, Jude!" And with his long needle Sam began rapidly to draw the gaping wound together.

"Here, Byrd, you hold Jude," I said, suddenly; and giving the halter to the dirty fledgling, who was snubbing tears in his distress over the accident to his old friend, I quit the scene of the operation and fled to the woods to faint down on a log and be as ill as I wanted to. It was rather bad; and it lasted about a quarter of an hour.

Then, with my head turned determinedly away from the barn, I sought distraction in an interview with my garden.

Oh, it was rapturous! Can anything in the world be as wonderful as putting queer little brown things in the earth, where it scares you to think of their getting all cold and wet and rotted, and then coming to see them sprout and curl and run out of the ground? No, nothing can compare with it unless it is seeing whole rows of them bursting out into blooms and tassels and little pods and burrs. I felt extravagant and wanted to kiss the whole vegetable family in a way of encouragement and greeting. And the two lilacs were both most beautifully plumed out in their long, white blossoms to greet me. Now, weren't they the plucky young things to bloom that way in a perfectly strange place? Still, everybody always did have confidence in Sam.

But then in every joy patch some weeds are bound to shoot up overnight, and I was horrified to look down the rows of purple beet fronds and see what a lot of bold pepper-grass and chickweed were doing in their trenches. Without waiting to get my gloves from my bag in the car, I fell to and began a determined onslaught. Furiously I charged down two rows and up a third, at whose end I sank with exhaustion.

"Say, Betty, could a cat give kitten dinner to a poor little duck that all the hens peck?" asked the Byrd, anxiously, as he came and squatted beside me with two of the new kittens and the duck orphan in question in his arms.

"No, Byrd, I don't believe so," I answered, from instinct rather than direct knowledge.

"Why is they so many little ones in the world without mothers, me and the duck and the cow that died 'fore Dr. Chubb came, her calf, and now that mean old dog have left her puppies to eat out of a plate?" he asked. He let the kittens slide to the ground, where they sprawled in their blind helplessness, while he began to tenderly pry open the small yellow ball's wide bill and insert crumbs of bread rolled into very realistic pills, but which the patient gobbled with evident appreciation.

"See, Byrd, you are just as good as a mother any day," I said, a choke in my throat as I cuddled his thin little shoulder in the hollow between my arm and my breast, and bent over to watch the orphan's meal.

"Like Sam," answered Byrd, with a queer little flash of his keen eyes up at me, and a grin that was so like Sam's that I tumbled him over onto the grass, duck and all, and began a frolic with him which delighted his heart and eased mine. I've loved that "little one" since the day they let me hold him in my arms when he was only a few hours old and motherless. Examining him from heels to head had comforted Sam in his anguish and eased my own sympathetic sorrow. It is a tradition that Mammy Kitty rescued him just in time; but I've always felt that nothing would have happened to him at Sam's sixteen-year-old hands if he had been left for hours.

In the midst of our frolic Peter and Sam came on the scene, and as far as Peter was concerned it was indeed a transformation scene. Sam was very much washed and slick from some time at the wash-bench, and Peter was likewise, only Peter was not the Peter whom I had brought from town that very morning. He was attired in a pair of Sam's overalls that could have been wrapped around him twice, and he had a bit of color in his cheeks under his eyes, though the eyes were slightly dazed as to expression.

"Good work, Betty, for only two hours," said Sam, looking at the three long ranks of slain weeds and then at his watch. "Pete and I are going to pick peas for to-morrow's market right after dinner. Want to help?"

I assented from pure ignorance, and we all went in to devour one of Mammy's chicken dinners, the like of which is not cooked by another person in the Harpeth Valley. The way Peter ate would have made the black beauty in mother's kitchen swell with jealousy until there were danger to her own black skin. Immediately after the gorge Sam gave me a basket, gave Peter another, and then looked around for the Byrd, with a smaller box; but the Byrd had flown.

"I'll have to tan him for shirking like that," said Sam, looking off into the bushes. "You Byrd!" But there was no response. That ought to have roused my suspicions, but it didn't. I went on down to that pea-patch as innocent as a newly born lamb, with Peter walking beside me, enthusing over the landscape and swinging the light basket with elegant nonchalance.

"I see, Betty dear—I see that there is a great satisfaction in the pragmatic accomplishment, and—" he was saying when we came out of the woods onto the southern slope, where lie the long rows of peas, which are making Sam's fortune. He got them in by working two days and all one night in a bright spell in mid-February, and nobody for twenty miles around has any, while he has more than he can gather to market at a top price; that is, more than he can gather himself with Byrd's assistance, he explained to us, as he showed us just how to snap the pod against our thumbs.

"I ought to put five barrels into Hayesboro every

day now for a week before anybody else gets any,"
he said, as he squatted at the head of a row between
Peter and me, and we all began to pull at the beautiful gray-green vines and snap off the full, green
pods. I looked across at poor, innocent, enthusiastic
Peter and saw his finish.

About three o'clock I saw my own finish, and
threw up the basket.

"You poor, dear child!" exclaimed Peter as he
came stiffly across the row Sam had long since
finished. He, Sam, was four rows ahead of us, and
a quarter of a mile away, more or less. I had collapsed, with my tired legs stuck out in front of me
and my thumb, swollen from snapping the pods, in
my mouth. "This is too hard work for you."

"Yes, it is; but Sam won't think so," I answered,
with a glance at the strong, broad back swinging so
easily down the slope. "Now, Peter, we must go
right along picking the peas. Sam must get those
five barrels," I said, as I hastily scrambled up and
began to pull at the vicious vines again.

"Well, I certainly don't intend to stop until they
are filled," answered Peter, stiffly, in more ways
than one, and without any more waste of sympathy
he turned his back and went doggedly at the vines.
That was my opportunity, and I took it. I rose,
looked with fear at the two men at work in front
of me, and fled, basket and all. I stopped long
enough to empty my full basket in one of the barrels
that were already in the wagon; and as I climbed
laboriously down over the wheels, with my paralyzed

legs working slowly, I caught a glimpse of a flash of blue out in the bushes, topped by a glint of red that was too large to be that of any bird inhabitant of The Briers.

"Byrd," I called, softly.

No answer.

"Byrd, do you want to go to town with me to see Mother Hayes?" I asked in subdued tones. That brought its response.

There were difficulties; but we surmounted them. We were afraid to wake Mammy at her afternoon nap for the clean clothes of civilization, so we purloined a fairly clean blue jumper hanging on the porch, while I left a note for Sam pinned on my old doll seed-basket hanging by his door. It was large enough for him to see, and it read:

I'm a good young mule, but I've broken down.   Poor Peter!
All that is left of
BETTY.

P. S.—I've rescued the Byrd for overnight.   I'll return him to his fate to-morrow.   Poor Peter!   Poor Peter!

I wish I could have seen Sam's face when he found it! The next morning mother's black beauty found my old grass basket full of delicious little peas on the front steps with this note in it:

You'll be docked a quarter of a cent every hour you are off your job.   Bring that brat home and both of you get to work.
SAM.

P. S.—Something is sprouting in your garden that I don't understand.

I knew those hollyhocks would rise up some day and bear witness against me. For the life of me I couldn't make up my mind what to say about them, so I sent the Byrd home by Tolly, who was going to take Edith out to see how her okra was progressing, and stayed in the safe shelter of my home. On the Byrd's rompers I pinned this note:

> Strike, if you will, my young back,
> But spare, oh spare, this little brat!
>
> BETTY.

There are all kinds of poetry in the world.

That night when I was beginning to get restless and wish I had gone out to my fate, even if it included being throttled with a pea-vine, Tolly and Edith came into town and stopped at my gate in such a condition that I was positively alarmed about them.

"Five baskets of peas!" gasped Tolly, as he fell forward limp over his wheel.

"My thumb! my thumb!" moaned Edith, with the afflicted member in her mouth.

"But, say, Betty," Tolly revived enough to say, "we are not going to tell Sue and Billy and Julia and Pink. They are going out to-morrow to call. Let 'em go—it's coming to 'em."

"Oh no, I won't say a word," I agreed, with the intensest joy. "Come over to-morrow, Edith, and let's finish *My Lady's Fan*. I'm dying to know what happened to her at the court ball. Good night!"

"No, you come over to my house; I'll be in bed,"

Edith wailed from the middle of the road as Tolly turned and made his machine buzz for home.

Then for five days — glorious, warm, growing, blooming days—I stayed in town in a state of relapse from gardening of which the sorenesses in the calves of my legs and my thumbs were the strongest symptoms, and listened to my martyred friends' accounts of what Sam was doing to Peter. I also had a bulletin from Peter every day by the rural-delivery route. That is, they were in Peter's handwriting, but they read more like government crop reports than a poet's letters to the girl to whom he considered himself engaged. I sent them on to Judge Vandyne, and I got a glorious written chuckle in return for them.

Then, one morning when I had about got over the bashfulness about the hollyhocks, and had decided to deny them absolutely and stick to it, for a time at least, I happened to pick up Grandmother Nelson's book. It was full time—maybe past time —for thinning out my sugar-beets and resetting my cosmos. I fled out to the wilderness in greater speed than I had left it, and fairly threw myself prostrate at the feet of my neglected garden. Peter helped me, a sun-blistered, brier-scratched, ragged Peter, whose face had lost none of its beautiful, lofty, aloof expression, but which was rendered almost ordinary by a long scratch across the top of its nose. The scratch was inflicted, he told me, when he held one of the thoroughbred Plymouth Rock biddies to be greased by Sam for lice under her wings.

"Yes, but what about the play, Peter dear?" I asked, after we had weeded and dug and watered and pulled up for an hour or two and had then seated ourselves at the end of one of the long rows to rest.

"The play—oh, Betty, it is—" And his old look of rapture shot across his face. Then Sam yelled to him, and me, too.

"Come on and help tie up onions," he called. "You Byrd!"

We went and we tied up—a whole white smelly mountain of them; but I didn't care, for Sam showed me his day-book, and in just one week his balance had shot up like the beautiful pink pie-plant in my garden. A great big entry was from my beets that he had thinned and sold without waiting for me.

"I'll give you a check when they are all sold, Betty," he said, in a business-like way, and something in me made me glory in him and my beets. "And isn't old Pete hitting the agricultural pace in fine style?" he asked, as we walked out into my garden between the rows of my blush peonies which had been grateful for the bone meal, and had bloomed, though everybody who had given me the clumps had warned me that they wouldn't flower until the second season.

"But isn't he going to write, too, Sam?" I asked, a trifle uneasily. "Now, you know, Sam, if somebody had kept Keats alive as a perfectly good lawyer or bank clerk—or farmer—he wouldn't have been half as much to the world as he is as a sadly dead poet. Now, would he?"

"Well, Pete will know all about the vegetable kingdom before he makes entry into the heavenly one, and we'll see what he reports when the time comes. Just come over and look at the wheat in my north field." Sam answered my anxiety so easily that I let it slip from my shoulders as I went with him to sit on a rail fence on the edge of a gray-green ocean of future food and be perfectly happy. "It'll fill dinner-pails and give babies mother's milk," said Sam, as he sat beside me and smoldered out over his crop. "The Commissioner of Agriculture was out here five times last week, and a complete report on the whole place goes in to the Food Commission in Washington. Pretty good for a less-than-two-year-old farmer, eh, Bettykin?" And Sam tipped the rail enough to make me sure I was falling before he caught me.

I didn't answer—I just clung, but Sam understood and roughed my hair into my misty eyes and lifted me off the fence.

Daddy got me two copies of that Agricultural Commissioner's report, and I sent one to Judge Vandyne and pasted the other in the front of Grandmother Nelson's book. Little did I know that simple action of pride in Sam would bring such results to Samuel Foster Crittenden and to Tennessee, and even to perhaps the third and fourth generation, or maybe—

Daddy says that when a man owns a bottom field, a hillside, and a creek in the Harpeth Valley all he has to do is to go out and swing his hoe around his

head a few times and he'll have a living before he is
ready to harvest it. I don't know about that, and
I do know that since I came home in early April Sam
has worked like two men, and maybe more. But his
harvests certainly amazed even the oldest inhabitants, who had sat around at the cross-roads gro-
cery and spat tobacco-juice at the idea of his farming
by government books, with no experience. They
came to sit on the rail fences around his fields and to
spit out of the other side of their mouths before the
end of July, and I never went out to marvel, myself,
that I didn't step on that Commissioner of Agriculture, who couldn't seem to keep away more than a
few hours at a time.

As things grew and bloomed and burst and flowered
and seeded, Sam went calmly on his way of work
with the crops from dawn to dark, and Peter did
likewise. I never saw anything like his friendly
pride in every successful test of Sam's work. And
his own fat was getting packed on him at a rate
that beat the record-breaking red pig down in the
long, clean pens that Sam maintained in the condition of a sanitary detention hospital. Also Peter
never mentioned the play, I never mentioned it, and
Sam appeared to have completely forgotten it.

I didn't quite like for Sam to forget Peter's play
like that, and I liked it less when I heard Julia say
that she thought it was so fortunate that Sam had
cured Peter of being a poet, so he could go into his
father's office to learn to take care of his great fortune. Peter likes Julia so much that I think she

ought to have appreciated the great thing in him more than she did. When the copy of the *Review*, with Peter's poem on the Ultimate, came, he read the whole poem to her while she embroidered an initial in the corner of a handkerchief for him. The next day she told me that she couldn't understand a word about it, and that it made Pink mad because she wouldn't tell him what to say to Peter about it. Pink has grown fond of Peter, but he wouldn't try to read the poem after the third stanza. But Peter went on back to help with the rye crop, knowing nothing of all that.

Of course, I had all the confidence that there is in the world in Sam, but I, about the first week in July, again began to feel responsible to the world for Peter's play; and I might have made the awful blunder of remonstrating with Peter or Sam or both of them if I hadn't got into so much trouble with Edith and Tolly.

Now, Clyde Tolbot is a very business-like young man, and he ought to be respected and considered for it, but that is just what Edith doesn't seem to understand how to do. She wants to go on with her head level with the moon, and Tolly wants to get married in November, and I think he is perfectly right. He hasn't any family, and he says Edith's "highstrikes," as he calls her moods and tenses, and the food at the Hayesboro Inn, are making him thin and pale, and hurting the prospects of The Electric Light Co.

"She acts as if she thought I was a cinnamon bear if I put my paw on her fair hand. And she seems to think it is scandal because I wanted to buy that old mahogany sideboard that the Vertreeses had to sell when they inherited old Mrs. Anderson and her furniture from his mother," he groaned, as he sat on my side porch with his head in his hands.

"Tolly," I said, with firm conviction in my voice and manner, "you must do something heroic to shock Edith down to earth again, or into opening her eyes as those kittens daddy gave Byrd did on their ninth day. The evening of Edith's eighth day has about struck."

"It most certainly has, and about eleven-thirty at that," answered Tolly, sitting up as if about to rush forth and do what I suggested, though neither he nor I knew what it was. "But what is your idea of a heroic deed that will pluck the child Edith?" he asked, just as if I were one of the clerks out at the power-house and he was conducting a business detail.

"Well, let me see, Tolly," I said, slowly, while I ran over in my mind all the lover heroics I had ever heard of from runaway horses to the use of a hated blond rival. "You couldn't get hurt slightly out at the power-house, could you?"

"And ruin my boast that I have the most perfectly organized force and machinery in the state? Not if I know myself," answered Tolly, with business indignation and an utter lack of lover's enthusiasm at the prospect of getting his lady-love by a ruse.

"Well, I don't know what you are going to do," I said, limply, as I saw that none of the things that had ever been acted before were within Tolly's reach.

"I don't know, either," answered Tolly; and again his head dropped into his hands.

"What did she say the last time you asked her?" I questioned. I considered it my duty to get to the bottom of the matter, as I had been called in consultation.

"Ask her? Thunderation! I never have asked her! I've never got that near to her!" he exclaimed, in a perfect outburst of indignation.

Then I laughed. I laughed so that Tolly had to pat me on the back to make me get my breath, and a sleeping mocking-bird scolded outright from a tree by the porch.

"Why don't you do it by telephone?" I gasped.

"By George! that *is* the idea, all right, Betty!" Tolly exclaimed, with his face positively radiant. I had flung his love troubles into a class of affairs that he could handle. "I tell you what I am going to do. I am going to have my wire chief cut Edith's line and make me a direct connection with mine at about nine o'clock to-morrow morning, as that is the time he is in less of a rush with all the other things to attend to. Then I'll put it to her good and straight if she holds on to the receiver and hears me out."

"But Edith might go over to Boliver to visit May

Jessamine Ray for a week at nine o'clock to-morrow.
Oh, go do it to-night, Tolly!" I pleaded.

"And let that doll-faced girl at Central hear me?
Not much!" answered Tolly, indignantly.

"I didn't mean that," I answered. "Go to her
armed with your love, Tolly, and make—make her
listen to you."

"Armed with a sand-bag to slug her would be
more like it, if I expected to get anywhere with her.
No, you've hit it, Betty, and I'm going on down the
street and see just where that Morris line goes into
the trunk. Hope Judson won't have to run more
than a mile of wire to make that connection." And
with no more gratitude or good night than that
Tolly went down the street with his head up among
his telephone wires, just as Edith keeps hers in the
clouds. I hope some day they will run into each
other so hard that they will crash out ignition sparks
and take fire.

As I said, being so interested in Edith and Tolly,
and trying to get her to postpone her visit until he
could get the wires up between them both in a material and a sentimental sense, and also wanting to
let Sam and Peter miss me sadly, I let quite a few
days elapse without being in any of the events out
at The Briers. When I did go back I found that
things had happened.

"Where's Peter?" I asked, as Sam came to unload me and a huge bag of smoke iris that old Mrs.
Johnson had given me for my garden. There was
also Byrd's basket from mother, and a pair of small

alligators that daddy had got from Florida for him, having run out of natural animal inhabitants of the Harpeth Valley.

"Pete's off with the bit in his mouth—haven't seen him for three days," answered Sam as he lifted me and swung me way out into the middle of my own clover-pink bed. It was starred with sweet, white blossoms, having been treated according to Eph's directions and those of Grandmother Nelson's book.

"Peter off? Where? What's happened, Sam?" I exclaimed, with astonished anxiety.

"The play," answered Sam, calmly, as he lit his cob pipe and blew a ring of smoke. "It hit him in the middle of the night before last, and he wrote me a note. Mammy grubs him, and I haven't seen him since. I've paid the Byrd a half interest in the next young that happens to us not to go down the hill to the shack, and we're all just going on as usual."

"Maybe I'd better not go, either," I said, with awe and sympathy for Peter fairly dropping from the words as I uttered them.

"Betty," said Sam as he looked at me through a ring of smoke that the warm wind blew away over our heads, "you run just a little more sense to the cubic foot of dirt than the average, it seems to me. Come on down and watch them begin to cut wheat. It is one week ahead of time, so I can get all the harvesters and not a grain will be lost. They say it'll run sixty bushels to the acre. Think of that, with only a thirty-six record to beat in the Valley.

It is that Canadian cross. The Commissioner is down there, and so is your admirer, Chubb. He wastes many hours riding over here to see you when you are in town on frivolous pursuits."

"Frivolous!" I echoed as we went up the path back of the house; and on our way over the hill I told him about Tolly and Edith. Sam laughed; he always does when I want him to; but his eyes were grave after a second.

"The mating season is a troublesome time, isn't it, Betty?" he asked, as he swung me to the top rail of the fence, vaulted over it, and held up his arms to lift me down on the other side; but I sat poised in midair to argue his proposition.

"It ought not to be, Sam," I said, with an experienced feeling rising in my mind and voice at thus discussing fundamentals with a man that could break a wheat record and be attended by the agricultural envoys of the United States government. "People ought to sensibly pick each other from their needs, and not act unintelligent about it."

At which perfectly sage remark a strange thing happened to Samuel Foster Crittenden. He laid his head down on the rail beside my knee and laughed until he almost shook me from my perch. It made me so furious that I slipped past him and ran on ahead. I vaulted the next fence in fine style and landed among the Commissioner and Dr. Chubb and the tobacco-juice neighbors, who had come to see the output of the first book-grown acre. I did not speak again to Sam that day until he tucked in Dr. Chubb beside me for a spin over to Spring Hill, leaving the doctor's old roan for a week's complimentary grazing on Sam's east meadow of thick blue-grass, grown through a rock-lime dressing that all the neighbors had assured him would kill the land outright.

"Wheez-chekk! nice young buck for a husband," wheezed the Butterball as I shot down the hill from under Sam's big hand reached out for my hair.

"Sam?" I gasped.

"Women critters always back and shy, but they git the wedding-bit from a steady hand—and like it," he chuckled, still further. I felt as if I ought not to let Sam rest under such a suspicion, and that I ought to tell him about Peter. But just then he launched forth on a case of a spavined horse he had beyond the cross-roads, which he wanted me to take him to see, and I didn't do it.

I don't much like to think about the long, hot July weeks that followed. The whole of Harpeth Valley sweltered, and everybody did likewise. That is, I suppose Peter did, for not one glimpse did I or anybody else get of him. Sam says Mammy set his meals down in the doorway of the shack with one of her soft, soothing, "Dah, dah, chile," which was answered with a growl from Peter. That ended the events of his life at The Briers.

Sam worked early and late, and got tanned to the most awful deep mahogany. All of him held out pretty well but his heels, which he came in three times to have me fix for him; and once mother and

I had to dress a blister on his back that he got from wearing a torn shirt in the potato-field.

I was wild with anxiety about Peter and the play and the poor little heroine; I didn't know whether she was being murdered or separated for life from the hero. Still, it was good to have Sam to myself for long, quiet, hot evenings out on the front porch under the brooding doves in the eaves above us. Sam never talks much but he listens to me, and sometimes he tells me things from way down inside himself. And little by little I began to understand all about the things he had been too busy doing to tell me about.

"You see, it is this way, Bettykin," he said, one evening when the young moon was attempting to silver the dark all around us as we sat on the front steps, with mother away rounding off the second pair of socks for Peter. "There wasn't one cent of money for me to take Byrd and Mammy and make a start in New York. Even with the best sort of a backing, it is always a ten-year pull for a youngster before he counts in the world. I could have sold The Briers, but I couldn't make up my mind to do it, and then while I hesitated I—I "—he paused a minute and steadied his voice, while I took his hand and held on to it tight—"I got a call—a land call that I had to answer. God just picked me up and planted me here on my bit of land, and I've got to root and grow or—or dishonor Him."

"Oh, Sam, you have, you have honored Him," I said as I crept closer to his arm.

"I've been all uprooted and pruned, Betty, and I've lost—lost—you know! But for Him I must go on just the same and bear fruit." At the pain in Sam's low voice something in me throbbed.

"Lost? Oh, Sam, what?" I exclaimed, as I hugged his arm against my breast. "What's happened to you, Sam? Tell—"

But just here we were interrupted by a clatter and a clash of hoofs, a wild shout in Peter's voice, and a cheer in the fledgling's high treble. The biggest mule lurched up to the gate, and two figures took a flying leap from his back to the pavement. With a rush they swept up the path and brought up panting at the bottom of our steps.

"Peter!" I gasped, descending to be sure that neither of them was bodily broken or demented.

"It's across! it's across!" shouted Peter as he reached out his arms and grabbed me in a wild embrace.

"What?" Sam and I both demanded, though, of course, in a way we knew.

"The play!" exclaimed Peter, putting his head down on my shoulder and fairly sobbing out his relief. "Farrington is going to begin rehearsals from the first two acts I've sent him, and I am to go right on to New York with the third that I finished an hour before the wire came over from the cross-roads station. You'll go with me, won't you, Betty? I can't go without you and Sam." And as he hugged me close Peter reached out and grasped Sam's big hand that rested on his arm.

"Of course Betty will go, and I'll come as soon as I get the whole crop in," answered Sam in his deep, kind, strong voice that steadied all our nerves. "I knew you'd make it, Pete. I never doubted that all you needed was a bit of brawn to punch from."

"Peter—Sam!" I gasped, trying to get my balance as I felt as if I were being hurried through space without even being told where to. "I don't know. I—"

"I can't do without you, Betty," Peter said again, as he held me close and Sam withdrew from us for the distance of about two steps.

"Betty is the real thing, Pete, and she'll stand by when you need her. She always does," Sam said, in a quiet voice that sank down into the depths of my soul and made a cold spot.

"I—I—don't know. I—" I was just reiterating when daddy and Julia, with a plate of something, came through the gate and up the walk. They had to be told, and they had to congratulate, and then mother came out to see what it was all about. They were all happy and gloriously excited, and I was dead—dead.

Then Sam took Peter home because he had to pack and get into town for the morning train. I begged for the fledgling to be left with me, and Sam consented without even mentioning the string-beans to be picked or the weeds in the parsnips. He said good night to everybody before he did to me, and then started to go with just the farewell word, hesitated a second, and came back and roughed my hair down over my eyes with the greatest roughness he had ever employed in that action. It would have broken my heart if he hadn't.

"Betty," said the Byrd, as he crouched at my side with his thin, scantily clad little body hovered against my skirts, "you ain't going to no New York with Pete and leave me and Sam and all the poor little ones, is you?"

"Oh, Byrd, I'm afraid I'll have to!" I sobbed, cuddling him close.

"Well, then, damn Pete!" he exploded.

IV

THE BOOK OF LOVE

MOST men are only a fraction of the greatness that the world adds them up to be, but Farrington is a whole man and then a fraction over. I enjoy talking to him just as much as I do to Sam or anybody else who is doing interesting things in a perfectly simple way. When we talked about Peter and the play he reminded me in lots of ways of old Dr. Chubb when he gets on the subject of spavined horses or sick cows; of course I don't mean any disrespect to Peter in that comparison. I told Mr. Farrington the same thing, and he didn't laugh at all; his eyes shone out from under his bushy white eyebrows like two wise old stars, and he said he saw exactly what I meant, and that he hoped to meet Dr. Chubb some day. And I continued to feel enthusiasm for him even after half an hour's talk on the subject of his treatment of Peter, which Peter had led me to believe was atrocious.

"Dear, dearest Betty," said Peter, as he met me at the train on the first day of September, "how won-

derful to have you come just when I need you most!
I am in the depths of despair." And he looked it.

"Oh, Peter, is it about the play?" I gasped as I
fairly hung on to his arm while he was languidly
giving my traveling-bag to a footman. Peter looked
like a literary version of what Sam called "the last
of pea-time," which is a very vivid expression to a
person who has just seen her poor peas drop away
in the August garden. "What has happened?"

"I care nothing more about the play, Betty. It
is stolen from me," answered Peter, gloomily, as he
led me through the Pennsylvania Station and up
the steps toward the limousine, where I knew Mabel
would be waiting to eat me up and be in turn devoured.

"Why, Peter, what can you mean?" I gasped.

"I'll tell you all about it when I get you to myself. Don't mention it to Mabel—she doesn't
understand," he answered from behind his teeth as
he put me into the car and into Mabel's arms, and
also into Miss Greenough's.

But for all my joy at seeing both those dear
friends again I couldn't help being depressed by
every glance at Peter, sitting opposite me, looking
white and glum.

"Don't notice him—he's more impossible than
ever," said Mabel, once, when Peter leaned out to
be reproachful to the chauffeur for doing his duty
and keeping us waiting for the traffic signal. "I'll
tell you all when I get you alone."

Judge Vandyne met us at the lodge gate of the

great Vandyne home out on the Island. He, too,
treated Peter like a sick baby. I never was so
puzzled; and dinner would have seemed long but
for the fact that they all wanted to hear so much
about Sam and The Briers and the whole Harpeth
Valley. I never more enjoyed telling anything, and
even Peter's gloom lightened when I told him about
the fat little duck the Byrd had insisted on sending
him—alive in a box. Daddy was secretly expressing it to me, on the sleeping-car porter's kindly advice, when he saw it in my baggage.

"Well, well," said Judge Vandyne, as he came
into the drawing-room with us after dinner, "young
Crittenden is really getting to goal on that farm
question. I'm glad you sent me that report—it set
some big things in motion. I'll tell you about it
when I get you alone," he added, under his breath.
And that was another time that made me feel as
if I were a baby that ought to be sliced up to be
divided. As it was, Peter got me first, and I don't
blame him for being in agony. That is, I didn't blame
Peter, but neither do I blame Farrington, now that I
have talked to him. This was Peter's tale of woe:

"Stolen, it is absolutely stolen from me, Betty,
and I am helpless to protect the child of my brain,"
he began. The judge and Mabel had at last left
us alone, probably because they hesitated to have
Peter commit patricide and fratricide, if those are
the right terms for sister and father murder.

"How, Peter?" I asked, taking his hand with deep
sympathy.

"Betty, since the first three rehearsals I am not allowed even in the theater, and Farrington is a brute. I do not know what he is doing to my play, but I do know that he was at work on a horrible laugh in the first part of the first act that I did not intend at all. The leading woman is coarse, with no soul, and the star is a great hulking ass. I am wild and nobody sympathizes with me. Father has talked to Farrington, and that is why he wired to you. Oh, I know he wired or you wouldn't have come up to this inferno at this time of the year. That is one kindness he did me—it *is* a comfort to me—oh, Betty." And Peter put his head down on my arm that was next him and sobbed, as the Byrd does when anything happens to one of his "little ones."

I didn't blame Peter at all, for that play was his "little one" and his first. I just took it out in hating and vilifying Farrington, until I got Peter much comforted, even interested in hearing about the splendid price Sam had got for the north-field rye. Then it was time for us to go to bed, and I suppose it was best that it was too late for Mabel to come into my room to tell me her version of Peter's troubles. For that one night I sympathized fully with him. The next morning I was shown another side of the question. And I felt decidedly different about Mr. Farrington when he talked to me for a little while, alone before dinner the next day, and after Judge Vandyne had also had me in solitary conversation.

"You see, my dear young lady," said Mr. Farrington, with that twin-star smile in his eyes I have mentioned, "the very wonderful nature that grows and flowers such an exquisite young first play as this of our young friend's, is the undoing of the work and the producer, unless he is a heartless old brute like the one to whom you are at present talking."

"Oh, I don't think you are that now, not at all. I—I think you are wonderful, and I trust you with the play even though you haven't told me anything about what you are doing to it," I exclaimed in great confidence and enthusiasm.

"You are a wonderful bit lass yourself, and I trust you with my poet, even if you haven't told me just what you are going to do with him," he answered, and looked at me with the real affection, tempered with amusement, that daddy and Judge Vandyne and Dr. Chubb all use toward me.

I blushed and was just going to tell him that— well, I don't know just what I was going to tell him, but I am sure I'd have opened my innermost heart to him, for that is what he invites, when in came Peter and the rest, and we all went in to dinner. I didn't see the great dean of the American stage alone any more, but he whispered to me just as Mabel and Miss Greenough and I were leaving the room:

"Keep my poet easy, and you'll see what you see."

I am glad now when I look back on it that my presence did help Peter through the ordeal of that

two weeks. Also Mabel and I had schemes together
to take his mind off his dying child, which was being
operated on by Farrington to make it a success.
The best diversion, however, was Judge Vandyne's.
He asked me to make out a list of ten of Peter's
Hayesboro friends, for whom he would send a
private car over one of his railroads, to bring them
up for the first night of the play. That was to be
the 20th of September, and even then the bills were
up all over New York. I could see, from the way
Judge Vandyne was taking it all, that he intended
to make the best of having a poet for a son, and to
put it through with his usual energetic force.

Peter was perfectly delighted at having all his
Hayesboro friends come. He wrote them all
letters, and Mabel wrote them notes. After that
Peter got uneasy and made Judge Vandyne write
to everybody, and the next day he insisted that I
should write, too.

"Oh, I wish Sam could come, but I know he
can't," I said, with a sudden hurt place just where
I was about to swallow my mushroomed cutlet.

"Sam not come?" said Peter, growing white about
his mouth and throwing down his napkin.

"Oh, Peter, Sam didn't want me to say anything
about it, but he doesn't think it is possible for him
to get away and—and you know, Peter, Sam has
to buy the sheep he wants to put in the woods; and
I told you that another mule—"

"I can't, I can't stand it for Samboy not to be
here," said Peter as he pushed his cutlet away from

him, upset his glass, and turned over a vase that
in turn knocked down the center vase of roses, besides upsetting the composure of the butler and one
footman. I saw it was going to be a regular poetic
outburst, such as Mammy would have called a tan-
trum in Sam or me, and that Mabel was positively
scared and Miss Greenough much pained.

"Crittenden will be here," said Judge Vandyne in
a perfectly calm and certain voice. "Don't worry,
son!"

I knew he meant that he would lend Sam the
money, or I thought I knew that, and I felt perfectly sure that Sam wouldn't come. Nobody
knows Samuel Foster Crittenden as I do; and the
reason he is so congenial with his mules is that he
is so like them in "setness" of disposition. I just
raged at him in my heart, for I knew from the way
I felt myself how poor Peter wanted him; but I
controlled myself and went right on talking about
how I knew the others would come and how much
they would enjoy it.

"Julia has never been to New York. Won't she
be delicious?" I exclaimed as we came to her on the
list. Peter had put her first.

"Delicious is the right word," said Peter, and he
then launched forth in a description of Julia that I
would hardly have recognized, though I had been
born across the street from her and have loved her
devotedly from our second years. It is such a joy
to have two people whom you love appreciative of
each other, and I knew that Julia fully reciprocated

Peter's interested friendship for her. She had wept on my shoulder at parting from Peter, and had written him long and encouraging letters for me while I was going up to Nashville to have my clothes made for the trip to New York and trying to get a little time in my garden out at The Briers. I have to stop; I never let myself think of that parting with Sam and The Briers. Some things are too deep for words. Then to continue about Julia, I wrote her how to have her dresses made, but told her to get only one little traveling-hat and leave the rest to Mabel and me and Fifth Avenue. I also advised Edith and Sue to do likewise, but I knew Miss Editha would have Miss Sally Pride make her a new bonnet on the frame of the old one, and Peter said she would not be the "wraith of an old rose" in anything else.

It was glorious that Tolly and Pink could both come, though Billy Robertson was not sure. I did so hope that Clyde would get a real chance to open Edith's kitten eyes for her through some heroic accident of travel, and I was glad that Colonel Menefee was coming, because he would engage Miss Editha's attention away from Tolly's attentions to Edith and give them a chance to come forward out of their backwardness. The telephone scheme had failed, Tolly told me, because the wire chief had made a mistake and still left them connected at Central. "Central" is the little Pride girl, the milliner's youngest niece, and very pretty. Just as he was ready to begin firmly with Edith she sweetly said:

"Now your connection is good, Mr. Tolbot."

When I left home poor Tolly was really becoming embittered against the world and was absorbing himself in putting up a new telephone line over to Spring Hill. I told Peter how he ought to appreciate Tolly for leaving business in that state to come up for the first night of the play; and Peter said:

"Dear old chap; we must find the shibboleth that will unleash the hooded falcon of his soul." Isn't Peter wonderful?

If all the invited guests in Hayesboro were busy getting ready to do justice to the first night of "The Emergence," we were in the same state. Judge Vandyne was planning to give a dinner that night to his most distinguished lawyer friends in honor of Farrington, and daddy had promised to try to come. Of course, Peter was going to have a dinner of his own, to which he was inviting a lot of delightful friends to meet his Hayesboro friends, and they were having both dinners at the Ritz, so Peter could go in and make a speech to Judge Vandyne's party. Most of the friends had not come back from the lakes and the shore and their country homes, but were running into town for that one evening. It was all the most delicious excitement, but—oh, a place way down deep in me behind my excited breathing was so sore about Sam! I couldn't even think about his not being there, but I went on and danced and had a good time in sheer desperation. Sam had to plow and hoe and reap and sow for food, while we ate and drank it and made merry!

Then the first night came, and everybody was there looking in high feather, and some of them wearing very low dress. Judge Vandyne had taken all the boxes in the theater, and they were every one full to overflowing with loving excitement about Peter. I was in the second box on the right-hand side of the stage at the front, and Peter sat in the shadow back of me. Julia and one of Peter's classmates were just behind us. As the curtain went up Peter took a hard hold on my hand under my white chiffon scarf, and I heard him mutter under his breath:

"Oh, Samboy!"

I am not going to try to describe that play of Peter's. The newspapers used all the adjectives and things there are in the English language to express enthusiasm with, and I haven't got any left. I will simply tell about it.

When Peter had gone out and buried himself in the shack on the hillside of The Briers, that looked out over the Harpeth Valley, he had unconsciously buried that frozen hero in "The Emergence" and had gone to work and resurrected him in a kind of Samuel Foster Crittenden. Instead of being a complicated, heroic, erratic genius he was just a big, simple, strong young man who was doing his part in the corner of the world's vineyard where he had been sent to work. To help him Peter had written in a wonderful girl with a great deal of brains for one so young. Just the sort of woman that men like Sam and the hero deserve to have. She was so lovely that I caught my breath and—and suffered. But what made everybody in that theater laugh themselves happy was the essence of Hayesboro that Peter had distilled and poured into his characters. Everybody was so mixed up with everybody else that nobody could feel sensitive or fail to enjoy every character. I couldn't tell whether I was the girl that practised tango steps all the time, even when the minister (who had manners like those of Colonel Menefee and the Mayor of Hayesboro) came to supper, or the girl that always had a plate of hickory-nut candy in her hand and kept saying sharp things while giving everybody something sweet to take away the taste. Julia said she was that girl, but Peter indignantly denied anybody's being anybody, and then we all kept still. Just then the curtain went down on the second act, with the whole house in an uproar; and there was a call for Peter and Farrington.

Peter went and left me sitting there in the shadow alone, while he stepped out on the stage all by himself—the stage of his life. And, oh, I was so glad to be in the shadow all by myself, for I had been as happy as I could and it was beginning to wear off. I wanted Sam—I wanted him even if the wonderful woman in the play was going to have him in real life, too, as I knew would have to happen some day. Also Sam deserved to be there that night if anybody did, and he was way down in the Harpeth Valley working, working, working, it seemed to me, that all the rest of the world might play. I wanted him! I felt as if I couldn't stand it when Peter stepped forward, looking like the most beautiful Keats the world had ever known, and the whole house gasped at his beauty and kept still to hear what a man that looked like that would have to say. I stifled a sob and looked around to see if I could flee somewhere, when suddenly my groping hand was taken in two big, warm, horny ones, and Sam's deep voice said in the same old fish-hook tone:

"Steady, Bettykin, and watch old Pete take his first hurdle."

I took one look at a great big glorious Sam in all sorts of fine linen that was purple in the mist of my eyes, and then I was perfectly quiet, with no fish-hook at all in my arm or in my life. I heard every word of Peter's speech, and laughed and almost cried over the one Farrington made about the young American drama, with his arm across Peter's shoulder. I forgot all about Sam because he was there, and just reveled in being happier than I had been since I had adopted Peter and the play, now that it was successfully out of our systems.

And it *was* successfully out. Nobody who heard the thunder after the last act could have doubted that. The *New Times* the next day said it was "The burgeoning of the American poetic drama," and another paper said, "Bubbles fresh from the fount of American youth." We got the papers and read them coming home from Peter's supper-party over at the Astor, which his New York friends gave because they wanted to see more of his Hayesboro

friends. Everybody was there and the success of
the evening came when Pink Herriford told his mule
story. Peter made him do it, and everybody adored
it. And just as they were all laughing and exclaiming at the droll way in which he characterized those
resurgent mules, I looked down the table and happened to see that Clyde Tolbot was holding Editha
Morris Carruthers's hand in a way that anybody
who understood these matters knew from the position of their shoulders that such was the case.

"A taxicab lost us on Broadway at ten dollars per
second, and I made connection with her wires before
found," he whispered to me, as we all rose to go,
just as the night was also taking its departure from
New York. New York in the daytime is like a
huge football game in which a million or two players
all fall on the ball of life at the same time and kick
and squirm and fight over it; but at night it is a
dragon with billions of flaming eyes that only blink
out when it is time to crawl away from the rising
sun and get in a hole until the dark comes again.
It is the most wonderful city in the world to stay in
until you are ready to go home.

Sam hadn't been at Peter's supper-party, and
neither had Judge Vandyne, but I didn't worry
about that. I never worry about Sam. I just like
to know he is somewhere near and then forget him
—if I am allowed, which I am not if Sam can think
up some important work for me to do. At six
o'clock in the morning I laid down the papers with
Peter's triumph in them and rolled into bed, dead

with sleep; and before seven Sam had sent me a note that forced me to open my eyes and stagger up and on. It said:

DEAR BETTY,—Get a maid at the hotel to come with you to the following address. I need you badly. A reliable taxi is waiting.

SAM.

Horrible thoughts of somebody's having kidnapped Sam flashed across my brain as I threw on my clothes. How had he happened to come to New York, anyway, and then disappear right after the play? What kind of trouble could he be in, and how could I help? I looked in my purse and found only ten dollars, but I felt the roll that I always carry in my stocking and it still felt a respectable size. I never count money when I am spending it, because you don't enjoy it so much; and I had been away from home three weeks. Still, if I had to bribe or buy Sam out of anything, I could get more some place. I must hurry to do as he told me, and then he would direct me how to rescue him.

In less time than it would take most girls, as soggy with sleep as I was, to get dressed and down to a taxi, I was on my way to Sam. I forgot to get the maid to go with me; and, anyway, what was the use, with a nice young white man like that taxi-car driver? He said, looking at me so pleasantly that I was sure he didn't really mean anything, "It's early, isn't it, miss?"

I was so hustled and so dazed, and had such trouble in making the little new kind of hook-but-

tons on my gloves stay fastened, that before I knew
it we drew up at a queer kind of old warehouse down
in a part of New York where I had never been, with
a line of the ocean or the bay or the river or the
harbor, I couldn't tell which, just beyond. Then I
was scared, for instead of Sam being in danger, I
felt that maybe I was being kidnapped. I hesitated
at the curbing as I got out of the taxi.

"Through that warehouse and to your left you'll
find the gentleman. Good morning, miss," said the
nice taxi-man as he touched his cap and drove off
and left me to my fate. If I had had only my own
fate to consider I would have taken to my good
strong legs and fled, but Sam was also concerned.
At the thought of his needing me my courage came
back, and I went on into the long shed where queer
dirty boxes and bales and barrels and things were
piled. At last I came to a turn and stepped into a
low room that was almost at the water's edge. It
was still very early morning, and a mist from the
sea made things dim, but in a crowd of queer people
and bundles and voices I saw Sam standing and
looking perfectly helpless, while that Commissioner
of Agriculture stood over by the window, evidently
perfectly furious and growling out expletives to the
saddest crowd of pitiful people I had ever seen.

Sam was in his dress-suit with his overcoat off and
his hair in a mop; and in a faltering jumble of several languages he was trying to tell something to
a gaunt, fierce woman in a wide ragged skirt, a shape-
less, torn man's coat, with a faded woolen scarf over

her head. In her arms she had a baby, and a woman with a baby in her arms knelt beside her; while a dozen other women with children, ragged, pale, frightened little children in their arms, and at their skirts, hung in a sullen group back of her. A crowd of dejected, hungry, gaunt men stood to one side, and one very old man had his old woolen cap off his white head, which I could see was bowed in prayer. In a moment I knew from their Flemish patois, which I had heard so often out in the fields of beautiful Belgium during that happy month just before the war, that they were refugees, and my heart went out in a rush to them as I went in a rush to Sam and grasped his arm.

"Oh, what is it, Sam, and what do they want?" I asked.

"They are emigrants from Belgium. The Commissioner has had me appointed to settle them in the Harpeth Valley on lands near my own, for which he has options. I came on in response to his telegram to meet them to-morrow, but they were landed here on the dock at one o'clock in the night, because of a fire on the steamer. I came right down from the theater, but they are frightened and the women have lost all confidence in everything. They don't seem to want to go with me to the car that we have ready to take them to Tennessee. I can't understand them, nor they me, and I sent for you. You're a woman, Betty. See what you can do to comfort and hearten them and make them ready to go with me when the train leaves in less than two hours,"

Oh, I know I am young and have been sheltered, and don't know what it is to be shot at and killed, and have my children torn from my arms and to be hungry and cold. But women do understand other suffering women, and when I stretched out my hands to the fierce woman with her starving child at her breast, I knew what to falter out in a mixture of her own patois and mine.

"*Il est bon*—a good, good man. *Alle avec*—go with him," I pleaded.

"But it is a fine gentleman! No, we come to a master, to work that we do not starve. A land-owner," she said, and regarded Sam in his purple and fine broadcloth with fierce and desperate distrust that the other women also expressed with hissing breaths which brought surly growls of suspicious acquiescence from the men.

"But look, look!" I exclaimed. I turned to Sam and drew one of his big, farm-worn hands forward and held it in mine out to the fierce woman, behind whom the others cowered. There was the broad thumb, off of which the barrel of peas had smashed the nail. There were the deep plow-callouses in the palms, and the plow-ropes' hard gall around the left wrist. The fierce woman's somber eyes lighted; for the first time she looked up past Sam's velvety white shirt-front with its pearl studs, up into the calm eyes that were smoldering their gridiron look down at her and the whimpering women and children.

"And here look *encore!*" I exclaimed, as I drew from my breast the large silver "peasants' locket" I had bought in Belgium, perhaps in her own village, and which I always wear with my street clothes, and had put on even in the hurry of my summons. I snapped it open and let her see what it contained. Sam saw, also! It was a picture of Sam milking old Butter-cup in the shed. Just as he turned to call me to bring an extra bucket to feed the calf, I had snapped it. I don't know just why I had put it in the locket, except that it is safe to have Sam around in time of trouble.

"*Eh, le bon Dieu*—I see, I see!" she exclaimed, looking first at Sam and then at the locket. Then suddenly she clasped my wrist and looked at the two big, hard, live callouses in my own palm, that some kind of a queer prophetic sentiment had warned me not to let a manicure work on. Also, she saw the pea-thumb that still held a trace of the blister. In-tently she looked for a few seconds, first at me and then at Sam. Then with a cry of agonized joy she fell at Sam's feet, and I drew down on my knees beside her, while the other women crowded around, kneeling, too, as their leader bowed her tear-drenched eyes in Sam's big, warm hands. One woman thrust a tiny baby into my arms as she kissed my sleeve and leaned forward to clasp Sam's knees, while the old man who had been praying all the time spread out his hands in a joyful benediction. The men's sullen faces lightened, and they bent to take up their pitiful old bundles and baskets.

For a long minute there was a sobbing silence while the Commissioner blew his nose over by the window.

I clasped the little starved baby close and pressed with the other women against Sam's knees, and Sam stood calm over us all. I know, I *know* he was praying down away from the sea, across half the world, into his own everlasting hills, over Paradise Ridge.

"Good, Bettykin!" he said as he bent and raised me and the fierce woman to our feet. The others began to bustle and hustle the children, and men, brushing tears from faces that had begun to smile uncertainly, as if they had never smiled before. A big tear fell off Sam's own cheek as he roughed my hair with his chin under the edge of my perky little hat, and took the woman's baby from my arms, as well as her bag and bundle, to carry them to the car. He led the way, and we all trailed after him.

It was a strenuous hour that we spent getting them all settled in the emigrant-car the Commissioner and Judge Vandyne had ready to take them right on from the ship to Tennessee. In the midst of packing away boxes and bundles and seating and quieting babies and women, Sam told me in snatches the reason of it all. One of the great Belgian land-owners had written to Judge Vandyne, who was his friend, to find some suitable place to colonize twenty of his peasant families in America. The letter had come at about the time my copy of the government's report on Sam's farming had reached him. He hadn't said anything to Sam about it, but had got hold of the Commissioner and secured options on four hundred acres back of Sam's farm in the wilderness of the Harpeth Valley. He had fixed it all up before he offered Sam the commission of settling and farming these people on shares for ten years. It was a little fortune poured into Sam's hands, but he didn't seem to think about that at all. His mind was entirely occupied by the hungry, big-eyed babies and their sadly smiling, clinging mothers. He had a whole bunch of ripe bananas, with other fruit and food in proportion, packed in the train for the long trip to Tennessee.

"Why didn't you write me all about it, Sam?" I asked as I patted a sleeping infant over my shoulder while the mother jolted a big-eyed twin of the same variety. Sam was undoing a strap from a large bundle for the fierce woman, whose eyes now followed him like those of a great, faithful dog—or my eyes.

"It was all settled less than a week ago, Bettykin, and I—I wanted to surprise you and Pete at 'The Emergence' first night. This ship wasn't due until to-morrow, and I was to have had a frolic. I asked the judge not to tell you. I wanted to break it to you myself. And I did with a brickbat, didn't I—at daylight to boot?"

"Where are you going to—to house them all, Sam?" I asked, anxiously, thinking of the little house with the Byrd and Mammy and all the baskets and seed and things, especially the one iron pot that only held chicken enough for them and—

"Got a tent village out of the colonel's Menefee

Rifles' tents over by the spring. It will be fine for
them until I can divide out the land and set each
man to log-rolling his shack. Dad Hayes is finishing
the camp for me, and Chubb is helping to make
things all shipshape, also buying a fine mule for
each family. Oh, they'll have a great welcome, or
would have if only you were there." Sam didn't
look at me, but smiled gently at the fierce woman's
thanks and turned to another strap and another
bundle. Again I went dead inside, and I turned
away and hid my tears in the back of the neck of
the tiny Belgian in my arms.

"Just about five minutes before we put you off,
Miss Hayes," said the Commissioner as he came
bustling up to me, smiling with the same energy
he had used in swearing so short a time ago.

Surreptitiously wiping my eyes and swallowing
the sobs in my throat, I held out the baby to its
mother and began to say a halting "adieu" to all
of them.

Then an uproar arose. They had thought I was
going with them, and they clung and wept and
kissed my hand and begged in broken words for me
not to leave them, though in their conduct there
was not a trace of a lack of confidence in Sam. Of
course, nobody that knew Samuel Foster Crittenden
a whole hour, even in his dress clothes in the daytime, could fail to have confidence in him for life.
But those women wanted me, too, and they wanted
me badly. I had to be torn from their arms and
flung off the train. Sam did the tearing and the

flinging, and he did it tenderly. Just before the final shove, as I clung to his arm and sobbed, the big hand went to my hair, and he said under his breath against my ear:

"God bless and keep you, darling—and Pete!" Then he swung up on the last step of the train and left me—shoved off into a hard, cold world full of luncheons and sight-seeing and dinner-parties and plays and dances and suppers and lights and music and flowers and like miseries. At the agony of the thought I staggered into the huge waiting-room at the station and sank on one of the benches and closed my eyes to keep the tears from dripping.

At first I just sat dumb and suffering—reviewing all the wonderful and exciting and magnificent things I had been planning to do for and with Peter and all the rest of my dear friends who were then in New York having the times of their aristocratically rustic lives. I reminded myself of the shopping excursion Mabel and I were going to make with Edith and Julia on that very day. The responsibility of Julia's hats was certainly mine, for I had told her to wait to get them in New York, and she would surely need them immediately in the round of gaieties that had been planned for them all. Then, who could help being delighted at the thought of seeing Miss Editha and the colonel introduced to one of the follies at the Winter Garden? I knew that I would be needed greatly then, and had rather dreaded it; though from Miss Editha's pink cheeks at the supper-party the night before, as she sipped her champagne I had rather hoped that she was making up her mind to a time of it. And then the joy of watching united Tolly and Edith! And Peter, how he would need me to help him to be responsible for all the wonderful things that were going to happen to him right along, now that he was the success of the hour. Even the papers had begun to speculate that first morning on his "next play."

"I'm weaving the laurel wreath rapidly now to bind your tresses, am I not, dear, dearest Betty?" he had whispered, as he told me good night at the hotel only a few short hours ago. Yes, I was needed in life, even if not down in a brier-patch in the Harpeth Valley, Tennessee, and I must bear my honors and responsibilities with as beautiful a spirit as Sam bore his burden of Belgians. I would have all I could do out in the world, and he would have his life full in the wilderness; but we would be a thousand miles apart.

And just here a very strange thing happened. From the weak, cowering, sobbing girl on the bench arose a very determined, red-cheeked, executive young woman who walked over to the nearest ticket-office and demanded of the brisk young clerk what time the different trains left for Tennessee. She found that by going at ten o'clock direct through Cincinnati she could reach Hayesboro two hours ahead of that Belgian emigrant-train that was to go around through Atlanta. Then she went into the dressing-room and got her wad of money out of her stocking, bought a ticket and a Pullman berth, six

magazines, some oranges, and a little traveling pow-
der-puff for the end of her red nose, and seated herself in the train before she woke up and found she
was I.

Then I took a hand and sent Peter a telegram
from Philadelphia, though to this day I can't remember what it said; and I settled down to the day
and night and part of another day's journey with
peace in my heart and the courage to take whatever
was coming to me from Sam.

When you are doing a thing you know is wholly
wrong it is best to make up your mind beforehand
just what kind of a right action you are going to
claim it to be. It only took me until Pittsburg to
have my course with Sam mapped out. I was just
going to ask him fairly what right he had to go to
farming with a lot of strange and untried Belgians
and refuse to take me in, when I had proved myself
a good and faithful comrade and worker for him
ever since I could stand on my feet.

"I just want him to answer me that," I said
to myself, and went to bed in the berth at six-
thirty and didn't wake up any more until I was
at Louisville at eleven. I had been in New York
two weeks, and I needed sleep. The interval between that time and three o'clock, which was the
hour that I stood before mother and her latest
rose-crocheted mat, I spent in strengthening and
fortifying my position.

"Why, Betty!" said mother, keeping the place
open in the magazine she was crocheting from, but

kissing me so tenderly that I knew she suspected
something had happened to me.

"I came home because I had to, and I'll tell you
about it just as soon as I come back from out at
Sam's, where I have to go as fast as I can on business," I said, as I hurried out to Eph for Redwheels
and up to my room for my corduroys and middy
blouse. I knew Sam would get his new family off
at the station at the cross-roads. I wanted to be at
The Briers all established and at work when he got
there. I have heard lots of times that possession
is nine points of the law, and I was determined to
possess all nine.

In less time than it takes to tell it Redwheels
and I were spinning away out Providence Road.
I had gone out on that road in early April in search
of Sam, when I thought nothing could equal the
young loveliness of the valley; I had driven Peter
out when it was in its May flowering, and back and
forth I had gone through all its midsummering, but
it had never looked to me as it did when I came
down into it from a far country, in the ripeness of
its mid-September. All the leaves were still on the
trees and many of them still rich green, but there
was frost in the air, and along the edges of the early
sweet-gum and sugar-maple branches there were crimson and bronze trimmings. Most of the gorgeous,
molten-gold grain was in stacks in the fields, and ev-
erywhere for miles and miles were stretched the wig-
wams of the shocked corn, seeming to offer homes
for as many homeless as could come and ask shelter.

Goldenrod stood up stiff and glorious in all the fence corners, while gnarled vines, fairly dragged down with wild grapes, festooned themselves from tree to tree, some of which were already heavily loaded with their own big, round, blackening walnuts.

Along the road there was a procession of food-stuffs going to town in heavy old farm wagons with their overalled drivers. Wheat in bales and wheat in sacks was piled on wagon after wagon, and I counted eleven teams hauling in loads of shucked ears of corn that looked almost two feet long. Oh, I was glad to think that those people who had fled from a famine-stricken land would meet that procession as soon as they got off the train, and my eyes misted so, as I thought of the joy that must well up in their hearts, that I came very near running over an old pig mother who was waddling across the road in the lead of nine of the fattest little black-and-white sucklings I have ever seen, each one with his tail curled at exactly the same angle. Giving her a wide run I swung off into Brier Lane. The old cardinal that had been so cross to me all summer, when poor Redwheels's puff had disturbed his family, was trillingly glad to see me, and flew almost across my shoulder as he darted and whirled his welcome. And what should I meet in the middle of the lane, evidently off playing hooky where she should not have been, but Mrs. Buttercup and my young spotted namesake! I immediately climbed out of the car and greeted them both so affectionately that, with my arms around Mrs. Buttercup's neck,

I persuaded her to go back the way she had come,
while I drove along behind her at a suitable snail's
pace. I had to stop every once in a while, when
she turned around, to assure her that I knew it was
best for her to go home with her full udder, as Sam
would soon be there to be welcomed and with company to be fed.

After I had turned her into the south meadow
gate, opposite the cedar-pole entrance to The Briers, I went up the hill at a lightning pace because
the nearer I got to the fledgling and my garden the
more anxious I was for a reunion with them both.
I met the garden first, as I rounded up in front of
the old hovering, red-roofed house that looked more
like home to me than any building I had ever seen
in my short and eventful life.

There is no love in the world that reciprocates
like that of a garden. If you work and love and
plan for it, promptly it turns around and over and
gives back a hundredfold more than you put into
it. All summer long we had been digging out of,
picking from, and cutting off of that little plot of
ground, and there it was reaching out with more
to return to me. Long rows of white and purple
cosmos danced and fluttered round-eyed blossoms
in welcome, while some bronze xenias fairly bobbed
over and kissed my rough garden boots. Miss
Editha's cock's-combs strutted in a gorgeous row
down the east walk, and what could have been a
greater surprise than that handed me by a row of
jolly round squash, though I had been sure we had

picked the last languishing fluted fruit from the vine the last week of August? But there lay long green vines completely resuscitated by the September rains; and nestled among their draperies of huge leaves were squash and squash, also big yellow blossoms and small green-yellow buds. I was so perfectly delighted at the recovery of my friends that I reached down and patted one of their head branches with its green tendril curls. There were a lot of gorgeous nasturtiums under the window of the living-room; but, of course, nobody expects more of nasturtiums than for them to be faithful unto death by frost. However, I did pick off a red one and proceed to chew it up with the deepest appreciation of its peppery flavor. And as I chewed with smarting tongue I cast my eyes along a row of beans that was fairly loaded with snaps, which made my thumb smart in anticipation of their gathering, until my gaze was suddenly arrested by something that sent me flying down the walk to the south end of the garden.

Now, a few weeks after I had hastily planted those hollyhock seeds Sam and I had sentimentalized over, I had found in Grandmother Nelson's book that hollyhocks never bloom their first season, but have to root and grow about twenty-four months before they blossom; and, somehow, that depressed me because everything in the world seemed slow at that time. How did I know where I would be after all that time, or that I would ever see them bloom, though they were making great leafy heads which both Sam and I strenuously ignored, while every time I went to dig around their roots somebody had done it before me! There they were, perfectly huge with their great fluted leaves, and right at the end of the row an extra-large plant had sent up a tall, green spike on the end of which a great, pink doll-blossom was shaking out her rosy skirts in the afternoon sun. I stood for a minute looking at her in utter rapture. Then I reached out my arms and gathered her in and put a kiss right in the center of her sweet heart. After that I fled to the barn in search of the fledgling.

I found him sheltering in his small jacket five little late chicks that would insist in running out from under the old hen, who was busily engaged hatching out their small brothers and sisters. He was afraid they would get fatally chilled.

"I needed you bad, Betty, if any more of these little ones was to act crazy like this," he said as I cautiously embraced him and his downy babies. "Put these three in your jacket so I can catch the next one that comes out. Old Dommie is 'most through, and then she can take them all." His faith in old Dommie, who to my certain knowledge had hatched two other families since spring, was not misplaced. In less than a half-hour all egg debris of the family advent had been removed and the babies put to bed under her breast and subjected to a sharp peck of her controlling bill.

By this time the sun had begun to drop down over toward Old Harpeth, and a lovely purple was stealing all over the place which mingled with a great veil of blue smoke from over by the spring, where, I felt sure, Dr. Chubb had lighted twenty new altar fires for the welcome of the home-comers. I wanted to go and see the camp, but someway I felt that it was time to go to the gate to meet Sam and his great big children, so down the Byrd and I went. When we got to the gate they were not in sight, and we started up Brier Lane to meet them. In my heart there was not the least particle of doubt that they would all be glad to see me, but I never expected it to happen as it did. Just as we came to the bend in Brier Lane that skirts around the first hill I heard beautiful voices raised in a weird joy-chant, and in a moment they all came into view, all walking and singing, with their things piled high on the wagons that followed them. In the midst of the tumbling, frolicking children, the chattering, pointing, exclaiming women, and the eagerly questioning men strode Sam with a small girl pickaback across his broad shoulders and the old praying-man walking by his side in deep conversation. I stood still to wait and let them all see me. The result was glorious. I had never known anything like it before. The women all laughed and cried in their excitable foreign way, and the men's faces showed great white teeth in radiant smiles. They kissed my hands and even the sleeves of my dress, and some of the children danced around and around in a very ecstasy of welcome, for I felt sure that to them I was the keeper of mammoth banana-bags. And I laughed and sniffed and patted and hugged the women in return, and nodded and called broken Belgian-English greeting to the men—to all but Sam. Sam stood perfectly still in the middle of the lane in the exact place that he had been when he caught sight of me coming out of the sunset toward him. He let the child slip from his shoulders and never took his eyes off me during the five minutes of the re-union rejoicings. And I never looked at or spoke to Sam, but walked on back to The Briers ahead of him, with the women chattering and gesticulating around me.

When we came to the gate I waited for Sam to come forward to open it. I wanted him to lead his flock into their promised land and—and I wanted to follow at his heels with them.

Around up the hill he led us, down the old road, past the big rock spring-house with its nine crocks of milk that I could see the women eagerly point out to one another, and into the little town of tents, at whose entrance stood daddy and Dr. Chubb, with their sleeves rolled up and energetic welcome in their eyes.

Then for an hour there was sorting of bundles and bedding; locating and housing; assuring and re-assuring; nursing babies by camp-fires, and feeding little mouths out of the huge chicken-dumpling pots that Mammy, with Dr. Chubb's assistance, had been brewing since morning. A big heap of coals was shoveled off a perfect mound of corn-pones; and there was plenty for all and some left over. I think I never saw anything so happy as the fledgling as he squatted on the ground and fed two toddlers from a bowl of corn-bread and gravy, strictly turn-about, the odd one to his own mouth.

Then, as the twilight came down softly like a beautiful benediction, we left them all, strangers in a strange land, fed, housed, and comforted.

We went up to the old white, hovering house, and while Mammy and I planned and in a measure mixed breakfast for the multitude down the hill, daddy and Dr. Chubb went with Sam, who had slipped on his overalls, to look at the new mules tied out behind the barn to long temporary stable poles. The Byrd I could not get from the company down by the spring. Later Mammy had to go down and extract him, fast asleep, from the midst of the largest Belgian family, where he was watched over tenderly by the fierce-eyed woman and the mother of the twins.

I had wiped the meal off my hands and taken off Mammy's apron when Sam came to the door and called me; and I felt very much as I used to when at school I went in to get my examination marks, as I followed him down to Peter's shack on the hillside. I wasn't one bit afraid of Samuel Foster Crittenden, I told myself, while I walked along behind him as he held the coral-strung buck-bushes out of my path; but my knees did tremble, and my teeth chattered so that I felt sure he would hear them.

For a long moment Sam stood in front of the shack

and looked out over to Paradise Ridge. I knew that now was the time for me to marshal up my defense and demand to be put on the same footing in life with those peasant women sleeping below us beside the covered camp-fires.

"What right has any man to say that a woman shall not plow and sow and reap and dig if she wants to, and especially if it is so much in her blood that she can't keep away from it?" I was just getting ready to demand. Then suddenly Sam sobbed, choked, sobbed again, and reached out his arms to fold me in against the sobs so closely that I could feel them rising out of his very heart.

"Betty, Betty," he fairly groaned, with his face pressed close to mine. A tear wet my cheek, larger and warmer than the ones which were beginning to drip from my own eyes.

"I can't help it, Sam," I sobbed. "I will be just as good as any of the other women; but I want a —a mule and twenty acres here with you. I don't feel safe anywhere else. I might starve, away from you."

And then, very quietly, very surely, I found out what it was I had been hungry for and thirsty for, what it was I had been used to having fed me ever since I could remember—it was Sam's love. He held me close, then closer for a long second—and then he pressed his lips on mine until I knew what it was to feel—fed.

"My woman," he said, when at last I turned my face away for breath and to get room to raise my arms around his neck and hold on tight until I could get used to being certain that he was there.

"I tried to let you give me away, Sam, but I couldn't," I said, with a dive into the breast of his overalls, which had that glorious barn and field—was it cosmic he told me to call it?—smell.

"When I've loved you a little longer I'm going to shake the life out of you for this mix-up," said Sam, hollowing his long arms and breast still deeper to fold me fast.

"I—I held Peter's hand all during that long play-making, and I can't stand it any longer," I said, squirming still closer and hiding my abashed eyes under his chin.

"Just hold my heart awhile now," Sam answered, as he sank down on the door-sill of the shack and cradled me close and warm, safe from the little chill breeze that blew up from the valley.

I don't know how long we sat there with arms and breasts and cheeks close, but I do know that some of the time Sam was praying, and I prayed, too. That is, I thanked God for Sam in behalf of myself and the helpless people in the camp below us and the rest of the world, even if they don't know about him yet. Amen.

Of course, it is easy enough, if you have a little money in your stocking, to cut any kind of hard knot and go off on a railroad train, leaving the ravelings behind you. But I believe that sooner or later people always have to tie up all the strings of all the knots they ruthlessly cut. Sam made me do it the very next day, after a long talk out on the front porch under the honeysuckle that was still blowing a few late flowers.

First he made me tell mother. She said:

"Why, of course, Betty dear, I always expected you to marry Sam, and I am so glad that you are so like my mother and will be a good farmer's wife. Did I give you that gardening-book of hers that I found? It might be a help to you both."

Did she give me that gardening-book which had made all the mischief? I felt Sam laugh, for I was hanging on to his arm just as I always did when he took me in to tell mother on myself. I was glad that she finished the eighth row of the mat and began on the ninth at that exact moment, so we could go on back to the honeysuckles and the young moon.

Then Sam made me tell daddy. Daddy said:

"Now I suppose I will be allowed to purchase a mule and cow or an electric reaper for that farm when I think it necessary?" And as he spoke he looked Sam straight in the face, with belligerency making the corners of his white mustache stand straight up.

"Make it a big steam-silo, first, Dad Hayes," answered Sam, laughing and red up to the edges of his hair—and daddy got an arm around us both for a good hug.

But the letter to Peter was another thing, and I didn't wait for Sam to tell me to write it. I smudged and snubbed and scratched over it all day and flung myself weeping into Sam's arms that night with it in my hand.

"Why, I wrote to Peter that night—the night I—I took you over, Bettykin. And here's the answer that came an hour ago by wire. Take your hair out of my eyes and let me read it to you."

I snuggled two inches lower against Sam, and this is what he read:

My life for your life, yours for mine, and joy to us both.
PETE.

I got a letter from Peter the next day, and it said such wonderful things about Sam that I pasted it in Grandmother Nelson's book with the Commissioner's report. I had to cut out a whole page about Julia's beauty and the way New York was crazy about her. Peter is the most wonderful man in the world in some ways, and I believe that, as he deserves all kinds of happiness, he'll get it; maybe a nice, big, pink happiness in a blue chiffon and gold dress that will rock his nerves through a long career of play-writing. I told Sam my hopes.

He ruffled my hair with his big hand, and my lips with his, as he smoldered out toward Old Harpeth. In his eyes was the gridiron land look that started the flow of sap along the twigs of my heart just a few months ago. Then he said:

"A man must plow his field of life deep, Betty, but if a woman didn't trudge 'longside with her hoe and seed-basket, what would the harvest be?"

THE END

STORIES OF WESTERN LIFE

RIDERS OF THE PURPLE SAGE, By Zane Grey.

Illustrated by Douglas Duer.

In this picturesque romance of Utah of some forty years ago, we are permitted to see the unscrupulous methods employed by the invisible hand of the Mormon Church to break the will of those refusing to conform to its rule.

FRIAR TUCK, By Robert Alexander Wason.

Illustrated by Stanley L. Wood.

Happy Hawkins tells us, in his humorous way, how Friar Tuck lived among the Cowboys, how he adjusted their quarrels and love affairs and how he fought with them and for them when occasion required.

THE SKY PILOT, By Ralph Connor.

Illustrated by Louis Rhead.

There is no novel, dealing with the rough existence of cowboys, so charming in the telling, abounding as it does with the freshest and the truest pathos.

THE EMIGRANT TRAIL, By Geraldine Bonner.

Colored frontispiece by John Rae.

The book relates the adventures of a party on its overland pilgrimage, and the birth and growth of the absorbing love of two strong men for a charming heroine.

THE BOSS OF WIND RIVER, By A. M. Chisholm.

Illustrated by Frank Tenney Johnson.

This is a strong, virile novel with the lumber industry for its central theme and a love story full of interest as a sort of subplot.

A PRAIRIE COURTSHIP, By Harold Bindloss.

A story of Canadian prairies in which the hero is stirred, through the influence of his love for a woman, to settle down to the heroic business of pioneer farming.

JOYCE OF THE NORTH WOODS, By Harriet T. Comstock.

Illustrated by John Cassel.

A story of the deep woods that shows the power of love at work among its primitive dwellers. It is a tensely moving study of the human heart and its aspirations that unfolds itself through thrilling situations and dramatic developments.

ZANE GREY'S NOVELS

THE LIGHT OF WESTERN STARS

Colored frontispiece by W. Herbert Dunton.

Most of the action of this story takes place near the turbulent Mexican border of the present day. A New York society girl buys a ranch which becomes the center of frontier warfare. Her loyal cowboys defend her property from bandits, and her superintendent rescues her when she is captured by them. A surprising climax brings the story to a delightful close.

DESERT GOLD

Illustrated by Douglas Duer.

Another fascinating story of the Mexican border. Two men, lost in the desert, discover gold when, overcome by weakness, they can go no farther. The rest of the story describes the recent uprising along the border, and ends with the finding of the gold which the two prospectors had willed to the girl who is the story's heroine.

RIDERS OF THE PURPLE SAGE

Illustrated by Douglas Duer.

A picturesque romance of Utah of some forty years ago when Mormon authority ruled. In the persecution of Jane Withersteen, a rich ranch owner, we are permitted to see the methods employed by the invisible hand of the Mormon Church to break her will.

THE LAST OF THE PLAINSMEN

Illustrated with photograph reproductions.

This is the record of a trip which the author took with Buffalo Jones, known as the preserver of the American bison, across the Arizona desert and of a hunt in "that wonderful country of yellow crags, deep canons and giant pines." It is a fascinating story.

THE HERITAGE OF THE DESERT

Jacket in color. Frontispiece.

This big human drama is played in the Painted Desert. A lovely girl, who has been reared among Mormons, learns to love a young New Englander. The Mormon religion, however, demands that the girl shall become the second wife of one of the Mormons—

Well, that's the problem of this sensational, big selling story.

BETTY ZANE

Illustrated by Louis F. Grant.

This story tells of the bravery and heroism of Betty, the beautiful young sister of old Colonel Zane, one of the bravest pioneers. Life along the frontier, attacks by Indians, Betty's heroic defense of the beleaguered garrison at Wheeling, the burning of the Fort, and Betty's final race for life, make up this never-to-be-forgotten story.

GROSSET & DUNLAP, PUBLISHERS, NEW YORK